Putting **Essential Understanding** of

Geometry and Measurement

into **Practice**

in

Prekindergarten–Grade 2

Karen Karp
Volume Editor
Johns Hopkins University
Baltimore, Maryland

Juanita Copley
University of Houston (Emerita)
Houston, Texas

Barbara J. Dougherty
Series Editor
University of Missouri
Columbia, Missouri

NATIONAL COUNCIL OF
TEACHERS OF MATHEMATICS

www.nctm.org/more4u
Access code: GMT14541

Library of Congress Cataloguing-in-Publication Data

Names: Copley, Juanita V., 1951–
Title: Putting essential understanding of geometry and measurement into
    practice, in prekindergarten-grade 2 /
Juanita Copley, University of Houston (emerita), Houston, Texas.
Description: Reston, VA : The National Council of Teachers of Mathematics,
    [2016] | Series: Putting essential understanding into practice series |
    Includes bibliographical references.
Identifiers: LCCN 2016027909 (print) | LCCN 2016043524 (ebook) | ISBN
    9780873537315 (pbk.) | ISBN 9780873539104 (ebook)
Subjects: LCSH: Measurement—Study and teaching (Early childhood) |
    Geometry—Study and teaching (Early childhood)
Classification: LCC QA465 .K27 2016 (print) | LCC QA465 (ebook) | DDC
    372.7/6049—dc23
LC record available at https://lccn.loc.gov/2016027909

The National Council of Teachers of Mathematics is the public voice of mathematics education, providing vision, leadership, and professional development to support teachers in ensuring equitable mathematics learning of the highest quality for all students.

Printed in the United States of America

Contents

Chapter 3
Decomposing and Composing Shapes 73

Chapter 4
Measuring Geometric Attributes 97

Chapter 5
Transforming Space and Objects 137

Chapter 6
Looking Ahead with Geometry and Measurement 159

Accompanying Materials at More4U

Appendix 1
The Big Ideas and Essential Understandings for Geometry and Measurement

Appendix 2
Resources for Teachers

Appendix 3
Tasks

Foreword

Teaching mathematics in prekindergarten–grade 12 requires knowledge of mathematical content and developmentally appropriate pedagogical knowledge to provide students with experiences that help them learn mathematics with understanding, while they reason about and make sense of the ideas that they encounter.

In 2010 the National Council of Teachers of Mathematics (NCTM) published the first book in the Essential Understanding Series, focusing on topics that are critical to the mathematical development of students but often difficult to teach. Written to deepen teachers' understanding of key mathematical ideas and to examine those ideas in multiple ways, the Essential Understanding Series was designed to fill in gaps and extend teachers' understanding by providing a detailed survey of the big ideas and the essential understandings related to particular topics in mathematics.

The Putting Essential Understanding into Practice Series builds on the Essential Understanding Series by extending the focus to classroom practice. These books center on the pedagogical knowledge that teachers must have to help students master the big ideas and essential understandings at developmentally appropriate levels.

To help students develop deeper understanding, teachers must have skills that go beyond knowledge of content. The authors demonstrate that for teachers—

- understanding student misconceptions is critical and helps in planning instruction;

- knowing the mathematical content is not enough—understanding student learning and knowing different ways of teaching a topic are indispensable;

- constructing a task is important because the way in which a task is constructed can aid in mediating or negotiating student misconceptions by providing opportunities to identify those misconceptions and determine how to address them.

Through detailed analysis of samples of student work, emphasis on the need to understand student thinking, suggestions for follow-up tasks with the potential to move students forward, and ideas for assessment, the Putting Essential Understanding into Practice Series demonstrates best practice for developing students' understanding of mathematics.

The ideas and understandings that the Putting Essential Understanding into Practice Series highlights for student mastery are also embodied in the Common Core State

Standards for Mathematics, and connections with these new standards are noted throughout each book.

On behalf of the Board of Directors of NCTM, I offer sincere thanks to everyone who has helped to make this new series possible. Special thanks go to Barbara J. Dougherty for her leadership as series editor and to all the authors for their work on the Putting Essential Understanding into Practice Series. I join the project team in welcoming you to this special series and extending best wishes for your ongoing enjoyment—and for the continuing benefits for you and your students—as you explore Putting Essential Understanding into Practice!

Linda M. Gojak
President, 2012–2014
National Council of Teachers of Mathematics

Preface

The Putting Essential Understanding into Practice Series explores the teaching of mathematics topics in K–grade 12 that are difficult to learn and to teach. Each volume in this series focuses on specific content from one volume in NCTM's Essential Understanding Series and links it to ways in which those ideas can be taught successfully in the classroom.

Thus, this series builds on the earlier series, which aimed to present the mathematics that teachers need to know and understand well to teach challenging topics successfully to their students. Each of the earlier books identified and examined the big ideas related to the topic, as well as the "essential understandings"–the associated smaller, and often more concrete, concepts that compose each big idea.

Taking the next step, the Putting Essential Understanding into Practice Series shifts the focus to the specialized pedagogical knowledge that teachers need to teach those big ideas and essential understandings effectively in their classrooms. The Introduction to each volume details the nature of the complex, substantive knowledge that is the focus of these books–*pedagogical content knowledge*. For the topics explored in these books, this knowledge is both student centered and focused on teaching mathematics through problem solving.

Each book then puts big ideas and essential understandings related to the topic under a high-powered teaching lens, showing in fine detail how they might be presented, developed, and assessed in the classroom. Specific tasks, classroom vignettes, and samples of student work serve to illustrate possible ways of introducing students to the ideas in ways that will enable students not only to make sense of them now but also to build on them in the future. Items for readers' reflection appear throughout and offer teachers additional opportunities for professional development.

The final chapter of each book looks at earlier and later instruction on the topic. A look back highlights effective teaching that lays the earlier foundations that students are expected to bring to the current grades, where they solidify and build on previous learning. A look ahead reveals how high-quality teaching can expand students' understanding when they move to more advanced levels.

Each volume in the Putting Essential Understanding into Practice Series also includes three appendixes to extend and enrich readers' experiences and possibilities for using the book. The appendixes list the big ideas and essential understandings related to the topic, detail resources for teachers, and present tasks discussed in the book. These materials are also available to readers online at the More4U website, where Appendix 3 includes materials and templates to facilitate hands-on work with students. Readers can gain online access to each book's More4U materials by going to www.nctm.org/more4u and entering the code that appears on the title page. They can then print out these materials for personal or classroom use.

Because the topics chosen for both the earlier Essential Understanding Series and this successor series represent areas of mathematics that are widely regarded as challenging to teach and to learn, we believe that these books fill a tangible need for teachers. We hope that as you move through the tasks and consider the associated classroom implementations, you will find a variety of ideas to support your teaching and your students' learning.

Acknowledgments

The author extends thanks to the following teachers, students, and schools for providing students' samples for the activities in this book:

- Dana Anderson's prekindergarten class in Yeager Elementary School, Cy-Fair Independent School District, Houston, Texas

- Jennifer Broadwell, Sue Peterson, Tina Bradley, Tracy Bass, and Tracie Wolffis's first grade students from Oehrli Elementary School in Montague, Michigan

- Trisha Hall's second grade students from Lincoln Park Elementary, Mona Shores School District, Norton Shores, Michigan

- Sara Freeman Morris and Elsie Contreras's prekindergarten students in Panda Path Early Learning in Spring Branch ISD, in Houston, Texas

- Students and teachers from ten Head Start sites in Houston, Texas

- Ann Franzosa's kindergarten students in Hazle Township Early Learning Center, Hazleton Area School District, Hazle Township, Pennsylvania

- Four amazing grandsons (in prekindergarten, kindergarten, first grade, and second grade), who attended Meme's Summer School in Muskegon, Michigan

- All the teachers who have provided students' work over the past twenty years!

Special thanks go to the writing team of Project M², funded by the National Science Foundation under Grant No. 0733189 developed at the University of Connecticut and published by Kendall Hunt. The author was privileged to work as a member of the writing team with four outstanding colleagues: M. Katherine Gavin, Tutita M. Casa, Suzanne H. Chapin, and Linda J. Sheffield. Although none of the student samples in this book came from the grant, the ideas that the team crafted certainly influenced the activities included in the book.

Introduction

Shulman (1986, 1987) identified seven knowledge bases that influence teaching:

1. Content knowledge

2. General pedagogical knowledge

3. Curriculum knowledge

4. Knowledge of learners and their characteristics

5. Knowledge of educational contexts

6. Knowledge of educational ends, purposes, and values

7. Pedagogical content knowledge

The specialized content knowledge that you use to transform your understanding of mathematics content into ways of teaching is what Shulman identified as item 7 on this list—*pedagogical content knowledge* (Shulman 1986). This is the knowledge that is the focus of this book—and all the volumes in the Putting Essential Understanding into Practice Series.

Pedagogical Content Knowledge

In mathematics teaching, pedagogical content knowledge includes at least four indispensable components:

1. Knowledge of curriculum for mathematics

2. Knowledge of assessments for mathematics

3. Knowledge of instructional strategies for mathematics

4. Knowledge of student understanding of mathematics (Magnusson, Krajcik, and Borko 1999)

These four components are linked in significant ways to the content that you teach.

Even though it is important for you to consider how to structure lessons, deciding what group and class management techniques you will use, how you will allocate time, and what will be the general flow of the lesson, Shulman (1986) noted that it is even more important to consider *what* is taught and the *way* in which it is taught. Every day, you make at least five essential decisions as you determine—

1. which explanations to offer (or not);

2. which representations of the mathematics to use;

3. what types of questions to ask;

4. what depth to expect in responses from students to the questions posed; and

5. how to deal with students' misunderstandings when these become evident in their responses.

Your pedagogical content knowledge is the unique blending of your content expertise and your skill in pedagogy to create a knowledge base that allows you to make robust instructional decisions. Shulman (1986, p. 9) defined pedagogical content knowledge as "a second kind of content knowledge . . . , which goes beyond knowledge of the subject matter per se to the dimension of subject matter knowledge *for teaching*." He explained further:

> Pedagogical content knowledge also includes an understanding of what makes the learning of specific topics easy or difficult: the conceptions and preconceptions that students of different ages and backgrounds bring with them to the learning of those most frequently taught topics and lessons. (p. 9)

If you consider the five decision areas identified at the top of the page, you will note that each of these requires knowledge of the mathematical content and the associated pedagogy. For example, using a shape in different orientations throughout an instructional sequence will support students' development of generalizations regarding the shapes' attributes. Your knowledge of geometry and measurement can help you craft tasks and questions that provide counterexamples and ways to guide your students in seeing connections within and among the multiple aspects of geometry and measurement concepts. As you establish the content, complete with learning goals, you then need to consider how to move your students from their initial understandings to deeper ones, building rich connections along the way.

The instructional sequence that you design to meet student learning goals has to take into consideration the misconceptions and misunderstandings that you might expect to encounter (along with the strategies that you expect to use to negotiate them), your expectation of the level of difficulty of the topic for your students, the progression of experiences in which your students will engage, appropriate collections of representations for the content, and relationships between and among geometry, measurement, and other topics.

Model of Teacher Knowledge

Grossman (1990) extended Shulman's ideas to create a model of teacher knowledge with four domains (see fig. 0.1):

1. Subject-matter knowledge

2. General pedagogical knowledge

3. Pedagogical content knowledge

4. Knowledge of context

Subject-matter knowledge includes mathematical facts, concepts, rules, and relationships among concepts. Your understanding of the mathematics affects the way in which you teach the content—the ideas that you emphasize, the ones that you do not, particular algorithms that you use, and so on (Hill, Rowan, and Ball 2005).

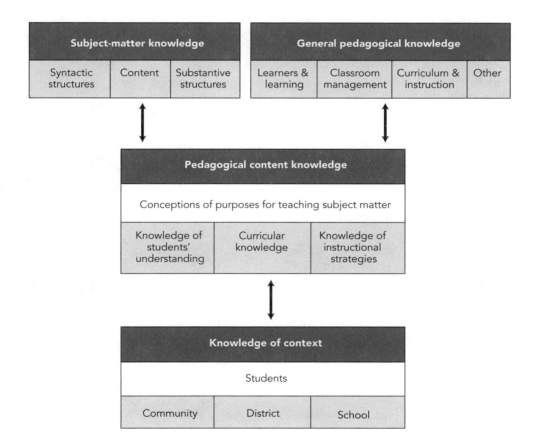

Fig. 0.1. Grossman's (1990, p. 5) model of teacher knowledge

Your pedagogical knowledge relates to the general knowledge, beliefs, and skills that you possess about instructional practices. These include specific instructional strategies that you use, the amount of wait time that you allow for students' responses to questions or tasks, classroom management techniques that you use for setting expectations and organizing students, and your grouping techniques, which might include having your students work individually or cooperatively or collaboratively, in groups or pairs. As Grossman's model indicates, your understanding and interpretation of the environment of your school, district, and community can also have an impact on the way in which you teach a topic.

Note that pedagogical content knowledge has four aspects, or components, in Grossman's (1990) model:

1. Conceptions of purposes for teaching

2. Knowledge of students' understanding

3. Knowledge of curriculum

4. Knowledge of instructional strategies

Each of these components has specific connections to the classroom. It is useful to consider each one in turn.

First, when you think about the goals that you want to establish for your instruction, you are focusing on your conceptions of the purposes for teaching. This is a broad category but an important one because the goals that you set will define learning outcomes for your students. These conceptions influence the other three components of pedagogical content knowledge. Hence, they appropriately occupy their overarching position in the model.

Second, your knowledge of your students' understanding of the mathematics content is central to good teaching. To know what your students understand, you must focus on both their conceptions and their misconceptions. As teachers, we all recognize that students develop naïve understandings that may or may not be immediately evident to us in their work or discourse. These can become deep-rooted misconceptions that are not simply errors that students make. Misconceptions may include incorrect generalizations that students have developed, such as naming a shape a *square* if the base is at the "bottom" but calling it a *diamond* if a vertex is at the "bottom." These generalizations may even be predictable notions that students exhibit as part of a developmental trajectory, as they learn and generalize attributes of classes of shapes.

Part of your responsibility as a teacher is to present tasks or to ask questions that can bring misconceptions to the forefront. Once you become aware of misconceptions in students' thinking, you then have to determine the next instructional steps. The mathematical ideas presented in this volume focus on common misconceptions that students form in relation to specific, interrelated topics—geometry and measurement in prekindergarten–grade 2. This book shows how the type of task selected and the sequencing of carefully developed questions can bring these misconceptions to light, as well as how particular teachers took the next instructional steps to challenge the students' misconceptions.

Third, curricular knowledge for mathematics includes multiple areas. Your teaching may be guided by a set of standards such as the Common Core State Standards for Mathematics (CCSSM; National Governors' Association Center for Best Practices and Council of Chief State School Officers 2010) or other provincial, state, or local standards. You may in fact use these standards as the learning outcomes for your students. Your textbook is another source that may influence your instruction. With any textbook also comes a particular philosophical view of mathematics, mathematics teaching, and student learning. Your awareness and understanding of the curricular perspectives related to the choice of standards and the selection of a textbook can help to determine how you actually enact your curriculum. Moreover, your district or school may have a pacing guide that influences your delivery of the curriculum. In this book, we can focus only on the alignment of the topics presented with broader curricular perspectives, such as CCSSM. However, your own understanding of and expertise with your other curricular resources, coupled with the parameters defined by the expected student outcomes from standards documents, can provide the specificity that you need for your classroom.

In addition to your day-to-day instructional decisions, you make daily decisions about which tasks from curricular materials you can use without adaptation, which tasks you will need to adapt, and which tasks you will need to create on your own. Once you select or develop meaningful, high-quality tasks and use them in your mathematics lesson, you have launched what Yinger (1988) called "a three-way conversation between teacher, student, and problem" (p. 86). This process is not simple—it is complex because how students respond to the problem or task is directly linked to your next instructional move. That means that you have to plan multiple instructional paths to choose among as students respond to those tasks.

Knowledge of the curriculum goes beyond the curricular materials that you use. You also consider the mathematical knowledge that students bring with them from their earliest years and what they should learn by the end of grade 2. The way in which you teach a foundational concept or skill has an impact on the way in which students will interact with and learn later related content. For example, the types of representations that you include in your introduction of geometry and measurement are the ones that your students will use to evaluate other representations and ideas in later grades.

Fourth, knowledge of instructional strategies is essential to pedagogical content knowledge. Having a wide array of instructional strategies for teaching mathematics is central to effective teaching and learning. Instructional strategies, along with knowledge of the curriculum, may include the selection of mathematical tasks, together with the way in which those tasks will be enacted in the classroom. Instructional strategies may also include the way in which the mathematical content will be structured for students. You may have very specific ways of thinking about how you will structure your presentation of a mathematical idea—not only how you will sequence the introduction and development of the idea, but also how you will present that idea to your students. Which examples should you select, and which questions should you ask? What representations should you use? Your knowledge of instructional strategies, coupled with your knowledge of your curriculum, permits you to align the selected mathematical tasks closely with the way in which your students perform those tasks in your classroom.

The instructional approach in this volume combines a student-centered perspective with an approach to mathematics through problem solving. A student-centered approach is characterized by a shared focus on student and teacher conversations, including interactions among students. Students who learn through such an approach are active in the learning process and develop ways of evaluating their own work and one another's in concert with the teacher's evaluation.

Teaching through problem solving makes tasks or problems the core of mathematics teaching and learning. The introduction to a new topic consists of a task that students work through, drawing on their previous knowledge while connecting it with new ideas. After students have explored the introductory task (or tasks), their consideration of solution methods, the uniqueness or multiplicity of solutions, and extensions of the task create rich opportunities for discussion and the development of specific mathematical concepts and skills.

By combining the two approaches, teachers create a dynamic, interactive, and engaging classroom environment for their students. This type of environment promotes the ability of students to demonstrate CCSSM's Standards for Mathematical Practice while learning the mathematics at a deep level.

The chapters that follow will show that instructional sequences embed all the characteristics of knowledge of instructional strategies that Grossman (1990) identifies. One component that is not explicit in Grossman's model but is included in a model developed by Magnusson, Krajcik, and Borko (1999) is the knowledge of assessment. Your knowledge of assessment in mathematics plays an important role in guiding your instructional decision-making process.

There are different types of assessments, each of which can influence the evidence that you collect as well as your view of what students know (or don't know) and how they know what they do. Your interpretation of what students know is also related to your view of what constitutes "knowing" in mathematics. As you examine the tasks, classroom vignettes, and samples of student work in this volume, you will notice that teacher questioning permits formative assessment that supplies information that spans both conceptual and procedural aspects of understanding. *Formative assessment*, as this book uses the term, refers to an appraisal that occurs during an instructional segment, with the aim of adjusting instruction to meet the needs of students more effectively (Popham 2006). Formative assessment does not always require a paper-and-pencil product but may include questions that you ask or tasks that students complete during class.

The information that you gain from student responses can provide you with feedback that guides the instructional flow, while giving you a sense of how deeply (or superficially) your students understand a particular idea—or whether they hold a misconception that is blocking their progress. As you monitor your students' development of rich understanding, you can continually compare their responses with your expectations and then adapt your instructional plans to accommodate their current levels of development. Wiliam (2007, p. 1054) described this interaction between teacher expectations and student performance in the following way:

> It is therefore about assessment functioning as a bridge between teaching and learning, helping teachers collect evidence about student achievement in order to adjust instruction to better meet student learning needs, in real time.

Wiliam notes that for teachers to get the best information about student understandings, they have to know how to facilitate substantive class discussions, choose tasks that include opportunities for students to demonstrate their learning, and employ robust and effective questioning strategies. From these strategies, you must then interpret student responses and scaffold their learning to help them progress to more complex ideas.

Characteristics of Tasks

The type of task that is presented to students is very important. Tasks that focus only on procedural aspects may not help students learn a mathematical idea deeply. Superficial learning may result in students forgetting easily, requiring reteaching, and potentially affecting how they understand mathematical ideas that they encounter in the future. Thus, the tasks selected for inclusion in this volume emphasize deep learning of significant mathematical ideas. These rich, "high-quality" tasks have the power to create a foundation for more sophisticated ideas and support an understanding that goes beyond "how" to "why." Figure 0.2 identifies the characteristics of a high-quality task.

As you move through this volume, you will notice that it sequences tasks for each mathematical idea so that they provide a cohesive and connected approach to the identified concept. The tasks build on one another to ensure that each student's thinking becomes increasingly sophisticated, progressing from a novice's view of the content to a perspective that is closer to that of an expert. We hope that you will find the tasks useful in your own classes.

A high-quality task has the following characteristics:
Aligns with relevant mathematics content standard(s)
Encourages the use of multiple representations
Provides opportunities for students to develop and demonstrate the mathematical practices
Involves students in an inquiry-oriented or exploratory approach
Allows entry to the mathematics at a low level (all students can begin the task) but also has a high ceiling (some students can extend the activity to higher-level activities)
Connects previous knowledge to new learning
Allows for multiple solution approaches and strategies
Engages students in explaining the meaning of the result
Includes a relevant and interesting context

Fig. 0.2. Characteristics of a high-quality task

Types of Questions

The questions that you pose to your students in conjunction with a high-quality task may at times cause them to confront ideas that are at variance with or directly contradictory to their own beliefs. The state of mind that students then find themselves in is called *cognitive dissonance,* which is not a comfortable state for students—or, on occasion, for the teacher. The tasks in this book are structured in a way that forces students to deal with two conflicting ideas. However, it is through the process of negotiating the contradictions that students come to know the content much more deeply. How the teacher handles this negotiation determines student learning.

You can pose three types of questions to support your students' process of working with and sorting out conflicting ideas. These questions are characterized by their potential to encourage reversibility, flexibility, and generalization in students' thinking (Dougherty 2001). All three types of questions require more than a one-word or one-number answer. Reversibility questions are those that have the capacity to change the direction of students' thinking. They often give students the solution and require them to create the corresponding problem. A flexibility question can be one of two types: it can ask students to solve a problem in more than one way, or it can ask them to compare and contrast two or more problems or determine the relationship between or among concepts and skills. Generalization questions also come in two types: they ask students to look at multiple examples or cases and find a pattern or make observations, or they ask them to create a specific example of a rule, conjecture, or pattern. Figure 0.3 provides examples of reversibility, flexibility, and generalization questions related to geometry and measurement in prekindergarten–grade 2.

Type of question	Example
Reversibility question	What shape has four angles and opposite sides parallel?
Flexibility question	How many different shapes can be composed with a parallelogram and a triangle?
Flexibility question	What shapes can be made by using three triangles? Four triangles? Five triangles?
Generalization question	What do you notice about the numbers that you count in your measurement when you measure a line segment first with inches and then with feet?
Generalization question	What are three shapes that might be classified as quadrilaterals? Why?

Fig. 0.3. Examples of reversibility, flexibility, and generalization questions

Conclusion

The Introduction has provided a brief overview of the nature of—and necessity for—pedagogical content knowledge. This knowledge, which you use in your classroom every day, is the indispensable medium through which you transmit your understanding of the big ideas of the mathematics to your students. It determines your selection of appropriate, high-quality tasks and enables you to ask the types of questions that will not only move your students forward in their understanding but also allow you to determine the depth of that understanding.

The chapters that follow describe important ideas related to learners, curricular goals, instructional strategies, and assessment that can assist you in transforming your students' knowledge into formal mathematical ideas related to geometry and measurement. These chapters provide specific examples of mathematical tasks and student thinking for you to analyze to develop your pedagogical content knowledge for teaching geometry and measurement in prekindergarten–grade 2 or to give you ideas to help other colleagues develop this knowledge. You will also see how to bring together and interweave your knowledge of learners, curriculum, instructional strategies, and assessment to support your students in grasping the big ideas and essential understandings and using them to build more sophisticated knowledge.

Students entering prekindergarten have already had some experiences that affect their initial understanding of geometry and measurement. Furthermore, they have developed some ideas about these topics in a variety of contexts. Students in the first years of school frequently demonstrate understanding of mathematical ideas related to geometry and measurement in a particular context or in connection with related topics. Yet, in other situations, these same students do not demonstrate that same understanding. As their teacher, you must understand the ideas that they have developed about geometry and measurement in their previous experiences so you can extend their knowledge and see whether or how it differs from the formal mathematical knowledge that they need to be successful in reasoning with or applying these ideas. You have the important responsibility of assessing their current knowledge related to the big ideas of geometry and measurement as well as their understanding of various representations of these ideas and their power and limitations. Your understanding will facilitate and reinforce your instructional decisions. Teaching the big mathematical ideas and helping students develop essential understandings related to geometry and measurement are obviously very challenging and complex tasks.

practice

Chapter 1
Classifying Objects

Big Idea 1
A classification scheme specifies for a space or the objects within it the properties that are relevant to particular goals and intentions.

Essential Understanding 1*a*
Mathematical classification extends and refines everyday categorization by making more precise what we mean by "sides," "angles," "straightness," or other features that we attend to as we categorize mathematical objects.

Essential Understanding 1*b*
We may classify the same collection of objects in different ways.

This chapter addresses the most familiar topic of early elementary school geometry—classifying and naming shapes. Even before entering preschool, most children have been taught to identify circles, triangles (in limited ways; they are usually shown examples of regular triangles and always in the same orientation), and rectangles and squares (typically taught incorrectly as two discrete shapes). Those who assess young children before they enter school to decide whether they are ready for pre-kindergarten or kindergarten often hear parents say, "My child is ready for school because she can count up to 10, and she can identify circles, triangles, squares, and rectangles." This type of knowledge, easily recognized and described by parents and teachers alike, is only a small part of the understanding that Big Idea 1 of geometry and measurement encompasses, and it typically represents knowledge taught only as definitions related to regular shapes.

Working toward Big Idea 1 through Essential Understandings 1*a* and 1*b*

In *Developing Essential Understanding of Geometry and Measurement for Teaching Mathematics in Prekindergarten–Grade 2*, Goldenberg and Clements (2014) approach the essential understanding that lays the foundation for later learning in geometry and measurement by first discussing classifying and the reasons for classification. They emphasize the importance of identifying similarities and differences among geometric figures and connecting informal descriptions with increasingly more precise language as learners progress in their understanding. In this approach, language is clarified, connected, and refocused on the specific vocabulary that defines particular shapes. As the authors state, "A precise specification of the way that we are classifying a collection of objects gives us a definition for the objects in that collection" (p. 13). This approach to classification of shapes marks a major difference from the way in which names of shapes and classification have typically been taught. Rather than defining geometric terms first and then asking students to find examples of shapes that fit that classification, students are given a variety of shapes and asked to sort and classify them by using attributes that they observe. The teacher starts with experiences that her students have had and examples that they have already seen. Then, as students develop their classifications, she poses questions and makes comments on their groupings, first using their words and then progressing to more precise geometric terms.

Classification tasks that require students to sort shapes or solids according to their own systems and then describe their sorting by using their own informal language provide excellent assessment opportunities. This chapter examines five classification tasks that build on one another to help young learners advance in their understanding of, and development of language for, classifying shapes.

Task 1: Sorting and describing shapes and solids of different materials

Figure 1.1 presents task 1, an initial classification task. The materials for this task are varied, and each type provides different classification experiences. Students should work in groups to sort and classify sets of—

- attribute blocks;
- paper shapes;
- wooden shapes and solids; and
- plastic-straw and pipe-cleaner creations.

Sort and classify the shapes or solids identified below into groups. Use words to tell how you sorted the shapes.

Materials for this task:

- Attribute shapes (three colors—red, blue, yellow; four shapes—rectangle [that is not a square], square, circle, triangle [equilateral only]; two sizes—large and small [only one size is shown here])

- Paper shapes (a variety, as pictured)

- Shapes and solids (a variety, as pictured)

- Shapes created with plastic straws with pipe cleaners threaded through them (a variety, as pictured; straw pieces are 2 inches, 4 inches, and 6 inches in length)

Fig. 1.1. Task 1

Reflect 1.1 asks you to think closely about this task, attending to the way that the different materials might affect the words that students use to label their groups.

Reflect 1.1

Consider the classification task shown as task 1 in figure 1.1.

- How would you expect students to sort and classify the shapes or solids in task 1?

- What words would you expect students to use to label the groups when using each of the four materials?

The attribute blocks in task 1 provide examples of shapes that are most familiar to students. The properties of color, shape, and size are clearly defined, and young students typically begin to classify these shapes by at least one of these properties. The paper shapes provide students with opportunities to categorize unfamiliar shapes by using numbers of sides, curved or straight lines, or different angles within shapes. Sets of shapes that include both two- and three-dimensional examples introduce students to the differences and similarities between and among these shapes. The plastic-straw and pipe-cleaner creations are limited to three or four straws or pipe cleaners per shape (see Chapter 3 for more information about their composition), and their flexibility adds to the classification possibilities.

Eight students' responses to the various shapes and solids that they encountered in task 1 appear in figures 1.2–1.5. Figure 1.2, shows the work of two students—(a) Colin, a prekindergartner, and (b) Amanda, a kindergartner—in sorting and classifying colored attribute shapes, the first set of materials listed for task 1. When Colin was asked to sort the shapes into groups, he was confused. The teacher then placed the circle divider on the table and told him to "put the shapes that are all alike in this loop." The teacher's conversation with Colin continued:

Teacher:	I see that you have lots of shapes inside the loop. Can you tell me about them?
Colin:	Red is my favorite color [*pointing to the four red shapes, which appear as gray in figure 1.2*].
Teacher:	I see the red shapes. Can you tell me more about this one? [*She points inside the loop at the red triangle—gray in the figure.*]
Colin:	It's red.
Teacher:	Anything else?

Colin: It's red; I like it.

Teacher: I see some shapes that are not red, and they are in your loop. What are they?

Colin: They are circles [*pointing to each circle, leaving out the red circle—gray in the figure*]. . . I like circles too!

Teacher: Is this one a circle [*pointing to the red circle*]?

Colin: No, it's red!

Teacher: Oh . . . So how are these shapes all alike [*motioning to the shapes in the loop*]?

Colin: I like 'em!

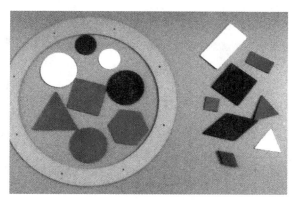

a. Colin's (prekindergarten) response

b. Amanda's (kindergarten) response

Fig. 1.2. Colin's and Amanda's responses to the attribute shapes in task 1 (fig. 1.1)

When Amanda was asked to sort the shapes into groups, she quickly responded by stacking the shapes as shown in figure 1.2b, and the teacher engaged her in the following discussion:

Teacher: I see that you have stacked your shapes. Use your words and tell me about them.

Amanda: [*Pointing to the circles*] Circles. [*Pointing to the squares*] Squares. [*Pointing to the triangles*] Rectangles . . . No . . . Triangles. [*Pointing to the rectangles*] Rectangles.

Teacher: Thank you. I noticed that you changed your answer on this one [*pointing to the triangles*]. Why did you do that?

Amanda: [*Laughing*] I always get them mixed up!

Teacher: I know a child in a different class who gets mixed up about triangles. Can you tell her why this is a triangle?

Amanda: See [*picking it up and rotating her fingers in a quick clockwise motion around the perimeter*] . . . It has three!

Teacher: Three?

Amanda: You know . . . Three points!

Figure 1.3 shows the work of (a) a first grader, Cooper, and (b) a kindergartner, Jennifer, in sorting and classifying paper shapes, the second set of materials in task 1. Cooper grouped the two paper shapes shown in figure 1.3a and labeled them "hexagon." To illustrate his label, he drew a hexagon of his own. He also said, "The long one isn't a very good hexagon, and the good one should also be colored yellow." When he was asked, "Why yellow?" he responded by showing a yellow pattern block. When he was asked why he had drawn his picture as he did, he said, "'Cause you can put green triangles on the yellow hexagon," obviously making another connection with the yellow pattern block.

Jennifer also explained her work, shown in figure 1.3b: "These are all triangles." She then asked how to spell *triangle*. When the response was, "Spell it how it sounds," she wrote *T-R-I-E-O-N-E-G-L-E*. She also noted as she pointed to the middle triangle, "See . . . Upside-down triangles are still triangles. My teacher said so!"

Two first graders, Armando and Juan, worked with shapes and solids in task 1. Their work appears in figure 1.4. Armando selected five triangular prisms and arranged them as shown in figure 1.4a. When the teacher asked him about these solids, he responded, simultaneously demonstrating what he was saying, "They all look alike . . . See! . . . They are fat triangles." Juan worked with his four-year-old brother, and as shown in figure 1.4b, together they classified their shapes as "not flat" (Juan's words) and as "cercles" (his brother's word) that are "flat" (Juan's word).

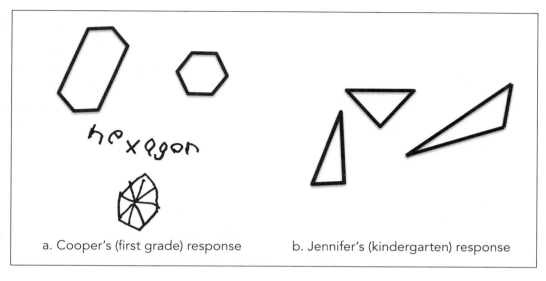

a. Cooper's (first grade) response   b. Jennifer's (kindergarten) response

Fig. 1.3. Cooper's and Jennifer's responses to the paper shapes in task 1 (fig. 1.1)

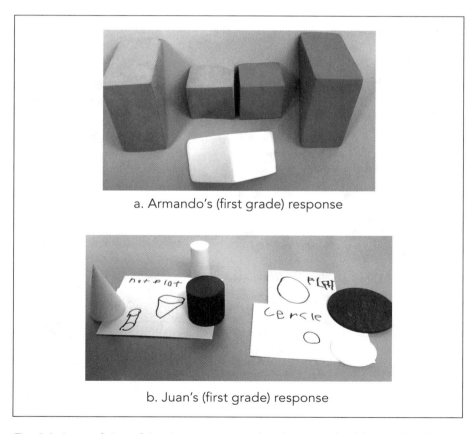

a. Armando's (first grade) response

b. Juan's (first grade) response

Fig. 1.4. Armando's and Juan's responses to the shapes and solids in task 1 (fig. 1.1)

Figure 1.5 shows the work of (a) a prekindergartner, Tucker, and (b) a second grader, Hong, in sorting and classifying the plastic-straw and pipe-cleaner creations in task 1. Tucker, whose work appears in figure 1.5a, identified two "tall" shapes and one "squ." He also drew them. When the "tall" shapes were repositioned horizontally, he said they weren't "tall" anymore. Hong identified two shapes, a kite and a diamond (spelled *D-I-M-E-I-N-D*), as shown in figure 1.5b. When the teacher asked whether the diamond shape could be called by any other name, Hong nodded and showed that if it were stretched out, it could be a square. He also demonstrated

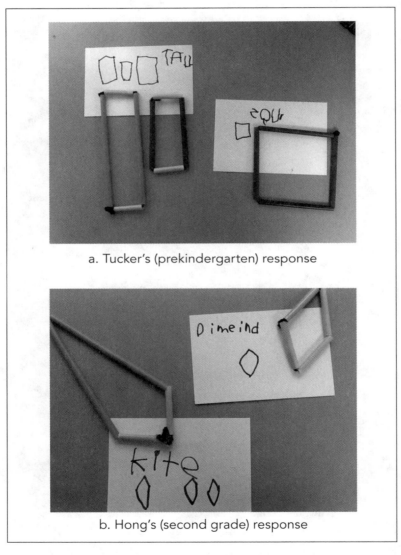

a. Tucker's (prekindergarten) response

b. Hong's (second grade) response

Fig. 1.5. Tucker's and Hong's responses to the
plastic-straw-and-pipe-cleaner shapes in task 1 (fig. 1.1)

that a rectangle could be "squashed" and then wouldn't be a rectangle anymore. He called it a *quadrilateral*.

Look back at the responses of all eight students, considering both what they did and what they said about their sorting and classification of the various shapes. Use the questions in Reflect 1.2 to guide your examination.

Reflect 1.2

- What would be your assessment of the students' understanding of shapes or solids on the basis of their work on task 1 shown in figures 1.2–1.5 and revealed in their descriptions?
- What questions would you ask or comments would you make to assess their understanding further?

All eight students whose responses have been shown and discussed demonstrated specific knowledge about objects and their possible classifications by labeling the shapes. Generally, these students labeled and defined shapes according to what they "looked like" rather than stating their properties. In addition, most students were selective about the shapes that they included in their groupings—that is, if the shape didn't fit in their system, they left it out. Except for Juan, who offered his "flat" and "not flat" classifications, the students did not use non-examples to clarify definitions of shapes. Several students sorted shapes according to non-defining properties. For example, Colin and Cooper specifically mentioned the property of color. Orientation came into play for Tucker, who described his "tall" shapes, and for Jennifer, who suggested that orientation was important to her response, according to her teacher's notes.

Equally important, all eight students demonstrated the need to grow in understanding and ability to clarify or expand their classifications of the shapes or solids with defining properties. In most cases, their reasoning indicated a partial understanding of shape classification and, in some cases, a misunderstanding of defining properties of shapes. For example, consider Cooper's (fig. 1.3a) response to the paper hexagons and his remark, "The long one isn't a very good hexagon, and the good one should also be colored yellow." The yellow pattern block is often shown as an example of a hexagon. As a result, students frequently think that a hexagon must be yellow like the pattern block and have six sides ofre equal length. When they are introduced to non-regular hexagons, they learn that the length of the sides is not included among the defining properties of a hexagon.

You can use students' responses to task 1 and your assessments of those responses in a variety of ways to inform instruction. Consider, for example, how you might apply these responses to help students develop more precise vocabulary and address specific geometric standards. Review the students' work in the figures and the descriptions of their responses again, this time with respect to the related expectations for prekindergarten identified in *Curriculum Focal Points for Prekindergarten through Grade 8 Mathematics* (NCTM 2006) and the relevant content standards for K–grade 2 in the Common Core State Standards for Mathematics (CCSSM; National Governors Association Center for Best Practices and Council of Chief State School Officers [NGA Center and CCSSO] 2010), as shown below:

Prekindergarten (*Curriculum Focal Points and Connections* [NCTM 2006, p. 11])

Children "examine the shapes of objects and inspect their relative positions. They find shapes in their environments and describe them in their own words," and use "objects' attributes that they have identified . . . (e.g., size, quantity, orientation, number of sides or vertices, color) for various purposes, such as describing, sorting, or comparing. For example, children sort geometric figures by shape, compare objects by weight ('heavier,' 'lighter'), or describe sets of objects by the number of objects in each set."

Kindergarten (Geometry [K.G], CCSSM 2010, p. 12)

Identify and describe shapes (squares, circles, triangles, rectangles, hexagons, cubes, cones, cylinders, and spheres).

3. Identify shapes as two-dimensional (lying in a plane, "flat") or three-dimensional ("solid").

Analyze, compare, create, and compose shapes.

4. Analyze and compare two-and three-dimensional shapes, in different sizes and orientations, using informal language to describe their similarities, differences, parts (e.g., number of sides and vertices/"corners") and other attributes (e.g., having sides of equal length).

Grade 1 (Geometry [1.G], CCSSM 2010, p. 16)

Reason with shapes and their attributes.

1. Distinguish between defining attributes (e.g., triangles are closed and three-sided) versus non-defining attributes (e.g., color, orientation, overall size), build and draw shapes to possess defining attributes.

Grade 2 (Geometry [2.G], CCSSM 2010, p. 20)

Reason with shapes and their attributes.

1. Recognize and draw shapes having specified attributes, such as a given number of angles or a given number of equal faces. Identify triangles, quadrilaterals, pentagons, hexagons, and cubes.

Refer to the questions in Reflect 1.3 as you consider the instructional implications of each of the responses and assessments in figures 1.2–1.5. Note that what *Curriculum Focal Points* highlights for prekindergartners can be paraphrased as "Children identify and sort shapes and describe geometric figures in their own words."

Reflect 1.3

- **How could questions, comments, or additional activities extend students' understanding of shapes and their properties while facilitating the use of precise language?**
- **How would classification activities relate specifically to the standards?**

Four topics or instructional strategies stand out when the understanding that the students demonstrated in response to task 1 is considered in relation to the recommendations in *Curriculum Focal Points* (NCTM 2006) and CCSSM—as well as suggestions offered by Goldenberg and Clements (2014):

1. Exploring examples and non-examples of shapes

2. Using right angles as a defining attribute of some shapes

3. Working with properties of three-dimensional shapes, including their two-dimensional faces

4. Classifying and reclassifying shapes on the basis of different properties

These four topics or strategies are important to incorporate into work with students and lead naturally to the development of tasks that use them to build on task 1.

Tasks 2–5: Using four fundamental sorting ideas to build on task 1

Tasks 2–5 are examples of tasks that offer experiences with each of the four strategies listed above. Many other such tasks are possible.

Task 2: Exploring examples and non-examples

Using examples and non-examples of shapes, including those that would be "near-misses," is an effective way to develop students' understanding of definitions and their use of more precise language (Goldenberg and Clements 2014). Exploring examples and non-examples of shapes, the first strategy suggested above as a way to build on students' learning from task 1, is the approach taken in task 2, shown in figure 1.6. Using the same collections of attribute blocks, paper shapes, shapes and solids, and shapes created from plastic straws and pipe cleaners as in task 1, task 2 requires students to sort objects into exactly two groups: one with items that *have* a particular property and the other with items that *do not have* this property. This approach is certainly responsive to the standards with specific references to key definitions at each level.

Task 3: Using right angles as a defining attribute

Introducing right angles as a defining attribute—the second of the four strategies identified above—can give students a way to build their understanding of a rectangle. A rectangle is a fundamental shape for students to grasp. Because a rectangle is a common shape in their experience, and because they frequently have a misunderstanding about a rectangle's definition, it should be part of any focused work on classifying shapes. Task 3, shown in figure 1.7, is an example of one such task.

In task 3, students are shown drawings of eight shapes and are asked to identify the rectangles by circling them and to eliminate the non-rectangles by crossing them out. Students often suggest that a rectangle can be defined as a shape that has "two long sides and two short sides." When they are introduced to a parallelogram that has two long sides and two short sides and no right angles, they immediately respond that it is not a rectangle because it does not "look like" one. The teacher then has an opportunity to introduce "four square corner angles" as a defining attribute of a rectangle. (See discussion of subtask 13f [pp. 110–11] in Chapter 4 for instructional suggestions.)

Task 4: Working with properties of 3–D shapes and their 2–D faces

Properties of three-dimensional shapes and their two-dimensional faces should also be a focus of geometric experiences for students in prekindergarten–grade 2. Focusing on these properties is the third instructional strategy identified above. Because students typically label three-dimensional shapes with the names of two-dimensional shapes, teachers should use more precise language as students complete making, tracing, modeling, or printing tasks. Task 4, shown in figure 1.8, is one example of such an activity.

Select one of the materials shown below: attribute shapes, paper shapes, wooden shapes and solids, or shapes made with plastic straws and pipe cleaners. Use all the shapes to make just *two* groups. Label one group as shapes that *have* a property and put shapes with that property in that group. Label the other group as shapes that *do not have* the property and put shapes without the property in that group. Explain your thinking.

Materials for this task:

- Attribute shapes (three colors—red, blue, yellow; four shapes—rectangle [that is not a square], square, circle, triangle [equilateral only]; two sizes—large and small [only one size is shown here])

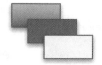

- Paper shapes (a variety, as pictured)

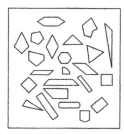

- Shapes and solids (a variety, as pictured)

- Shapes created with plastic straws with pipe cleaners threaded through them (a variety, as pictured; straw pieces are 2 inches, 4 inches, and 6 inches in length)

Fig. 1.6. Task 2

Circle the shapes that are rectangles. Cross out the shapes that are *not* rectangles. Explain your thinking.

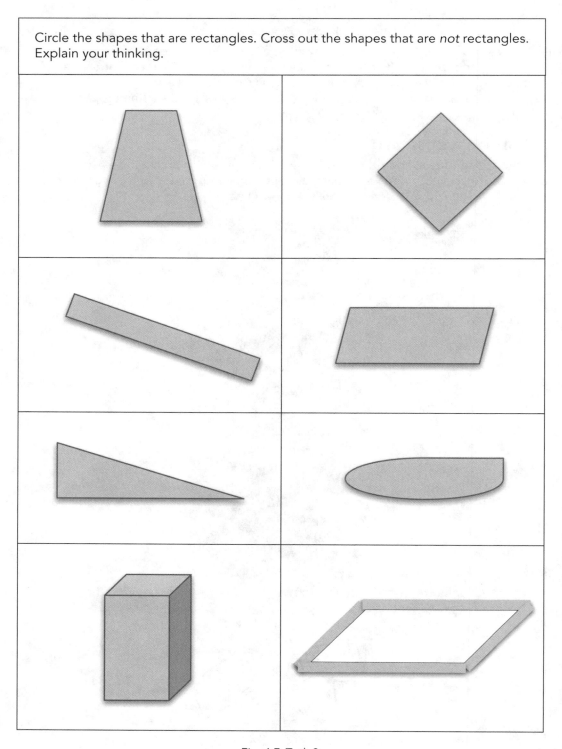

Fig. 1.7. Task 3

Make, trace, draw, and describe three-dimensional shapes.

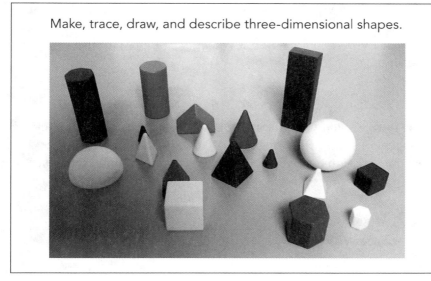

Fig. 1.8. Task 4

Task 5: Reclassifying shapes by using different properties

Students should also have many experiences with classifying and defining a shape, or many shapes, in different ways. This is the fourth instructional focus identified above. Consider task 5 in figure 1.9, for example. Just as a teacher has different names based on specific attributes ("Ms. ____" or "Mr. ____" to students, "Mom" or

Classify 2-D shapes in more than one way. Explain your classifications by using a Venn diagram (for example, two loops, each containing shapes with a different defining attribute).

Fig. 1.9. Task 5

"Dad" to a child, or "my wife" or "my husband" to a spouse, etc.), so do shapes. For instance, a square is a *polygon* because it is a closed figure formed by line segments that meet only at their endpoints, and it is a *quadrilateral* because it is a four-sided polygon, and so on.

Responding to students' work on tasks 2–5

Reflect 1.4 encourages you to think about how you might respond effectively to students if you were examining and comparing their responses to tasks 2–5. As you consider the questions, bear in mind the four topics and instructional strategies discussed in relation to these tasks.

Reflect 1.4

- How could you respond to students who are completing tasks 2, 3, 4, and 5?

- How do you think students would respond to your questions or comments as they completed the tasks?

An underlying goal of tasks 2–5 is to sharpen students' focus on the language used to describe shapes. Below are some general questions and comments for use in developing students' understanding and facilitating their use of more precise language. Examine these before considering the sample responses included below from students to the tasks.

- "How do you draw a _____?" [*Respond to whatever the students say by drawing only what exactly matches their words. For example, if they say, "A triangle has three points," draw only three points, with no line segments.*] "Is this a _____? What else do I need to include? How?"

- "You said that all these shapes are _____. So this should be one too, right?" [*Draw a shape that is exactly like the others but different in non-defining attributes, such as color or orientation. Also include some shapes that are the same in non-defining attributes, such as color, but different in defining attributes, making them different shapes.*] "Why or why not?"

- "Let's make a shape. Use your words to tell me how to make it. What would we call this shape? Why should it be called a _____?" [*Create with students a two- or three-dimensional shape, talking aloud and using precise language as the shape comes into being. Make connections explicitly between the words that students use and more precise geometric language.*]

- [*Point to a particular shape.*] "You said this shape is a _____. Jonathan said it was a _____. How are those two shapes different? How are they alike? Can they both be a _____ and still look different? Why or why not?"

- [*Draw students' attention to shapes sorted into examples and non-examples of a property.*] "Mary sorted her shapes into two piles." [*Indicate the shapes in the pile of examples.*] "All the shapes in this pile have the same property." [*Then indicate the shapes in the other pile.*] "All the shapes in this other pile do not have that property. Mary lost the card that identified the property. What do you think it is? Why do you think so?"

Figures 1.10–1.13 show a sampling of students' responses to tasks 2–5. As you consider their work, use the questions in Reflect 1.5 to guide you in assessing the students' understanding and misunderstanding.

Reflect 1.5

- Consider the students' responses to tasks 2–5 shown in figures 1.10–1.13 and discussed below. How do these responses reflect the students' understanding of the classification of shapes and solids?

- How would you change your instruction to facilitate increased understanding?

Task 2 (see fig. 1.6) calls on students to work with a variety of materials and sort a collection of shapes or solids into just two groups—those that *have* a particular property and those that *do not have* that property. Identifying, sorting, and classifying shapes as *not* having a particular property helps students to develop more precise vocabulary for discussing shapes. Understanding what properties a shape does not have further clarifies for them the definition of a specific shape and the properties that it does have. Figure 1.10 shows the work of two groups of students—(a) first graders who sorted a variety of paper shapes and (b) prekindergartners who sorted 2-D shapes including those made of paper and those constructed of straws with pipe cleaners threaded through them. The first graders whose work is shown in figure 1.10a made a puzzle by placing shapes that had a "hidden" property inside the loop and placing non-examples outside the loop. The hidden properties of the shapes inside the loop are that they are "flat" and have "sides of equal length."

The prekindergartners whose work is shown in figure 1.10b made a shape-sorting poster. They sorted shapes into two groups—those that are made with four straight lines (shown on the left side of their poster) and those that are not made with four straight lines (shown on the right side). Later the pipe cleaner "tails" were cut off

a. A one-loop puzzle made by first graders

b. A poster showing examples and non-examples,
made by prekindergartners

Fig. 1.10. Two groups' responses to task 2, using a variety of 2-D shapes

or wrapped around the straws, and the big word *quadrilaterals* was used to describe shapes made with four straight lines, connected at the corners. *Quadrilaterals* quickly became one of the students' favorite words! All the students who created the two examples shown in figure 1.10 appear to have understood the properties of "equal length" and "shapes made with four straight lines."

Task 3 (see fig. 1.7) asks students to look at eight shapes and circle those that are rectangles, cross out those that are not rectangles, and explain their thinking. Figure 1.11 shows the responses of two students—(a) Gordy, a prekindergartner, and (b) Daniel, a first grader—to this task. Both Gordy and Daniel were somewhat familiar with rectangles. Gordy appears to have had an understanding of what a typical rectangle looks like when he talked about the two lines "going up." He also pointed to the door, which he recognized as a familiar example of a rectangle. Daniel talked about "special square corners" that a rectangle has to have, indicating that he had been introduced to the idea of four right angles as the defining attribute of a rectangle. He applied that definition correctly to each of the pictured shapes with the exception of the square, which he identified as a "diamond."

Figure 1.12 shows responses to task 4 (see fig. 1.8) from students ranging in level from prekindergarten to grade 1. In this task students are asked to make, trace, draw, and describe 3-D shapes. The sample responses in the figure show how students become familiar with three-dimensional shapes by tracing, making prints, and drawing their own representations of these solids. Figure 1.12a shows how a prekindergartner, Devin, traced the bases of two cylinders. When asked what the shapes on the paper were, Devin replied, "Two circles!" Although students may not know the names of many three-dimensional shapes, they are often able to identify the shapes of the "flat" parts, or *faces*, and, in this way, they can begin to identify the parts to be measured later. Figure 1.12b shows the work of first graders who traced the faces of 3-D blocks during center time. When one student, Aimee, was asked to describe the faces of the square pyramid, she replied, "Three triangles and one square." Figure 1.12c shows the imprints made by a four-year-old in modeling dough of the faces of a triangular prism. Students in the group called the triangular prisms "fat triangles." Figure 1.12d shows a five-year-old child's two-dimensional drawings of three-dimensional shapes: a cube and a cylinder.

Figure 1.13 shows two responses to task 5 (see fig 1.9), which asks students to classify shapes in more than one way and explain their work. The responses shown represent two groups' efforts. Parts (a) and (b) show work from a kindergarten class, and (c) shows work from second graders. The kindergartners used loops to establish two groups: one for triangles and one for red shapes. (Unfortunately, the

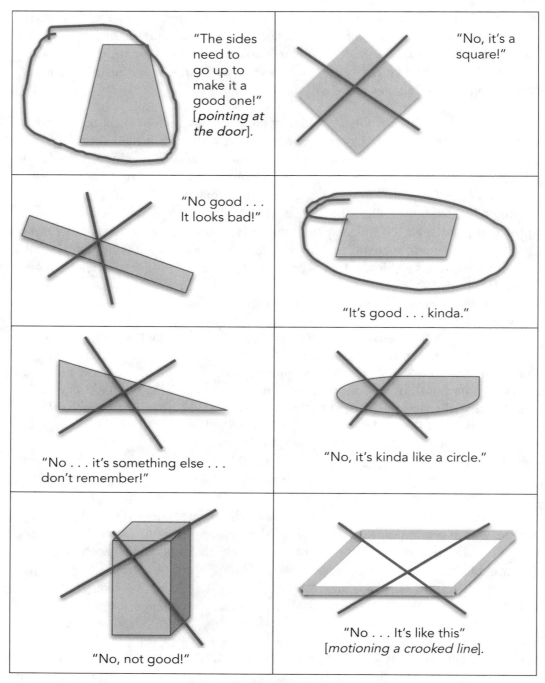

a. Gordy's (prekindergartner) response

Fig. 1.11. Students' responses to task 3, along with their verbalizations

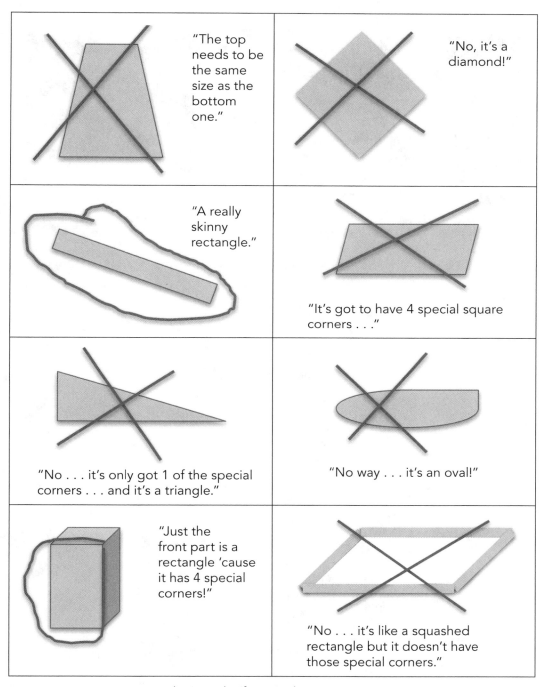

b. Daniel's (first grader) response

Fig. 1.11. *Continued*

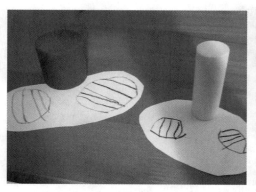

a. A prekindergartner's tracing of
the bases of two cylinders

b. First graders' tracing of the flat
faces of 3-D blocks

c. A four-year-old's imprints in modeling dough
of the faces of a triangular prism

d. A five-year-old's drawings of a cube and a cylinder

Fig. 1.12. Students' responses to task 4

figure shows all colors as shades of gray.) The students described their specific shapes and then decided where to place them. As shown in (a), they placed three triangles that were not red in the triangle loop (lower in fig.), and they placed two red shapes, a circle and a rectangle in the loop for red shapes (upper in fig.). They placed three shapes in neither the red loop nor the triangle loop. The last shape that the students analyzed was a red triangle. They debated where to put it, because

a. Two groups established by kindergartners:
one for triangles and one for red shapes

b. Kindergartners' placement of a red triangle

c. Two groups established by a small group of second graders

Fig. 1.13. Students' responses to task 5

they recognized that it belonged in both groups. They considered (1) cutting it in half and putting one piece in each loop, (2) putting the loops close together and placing the red triangle on the boundary, and (3) getting another red triangle. They continued to debate until someone suggested overlapping the loops. That worked, and figure 1.13b shows the result.

Figure 1.13c shows the work of second graders on the same task. The second graders used hula hoops to represent two groups. One student was in charge of the hula hoop on the left, which contained rectangles (in other words, four-sided flat shapes with four square corners). Another student was in charge of the hula hoop on the right, which contained rhombi (four-sided flat shapes with four sides of equal lengths). Faced with two squares, the students at first placed one in the rectangle hoop and one in the rhombus hoop in their Venn diagram, recognizing that they belonged in both hula hoops—in the rectangle hoop (because they are flat and have square corners and four sides) *and* in the rhombus hoop (because they are flat and their sides are equal in length). After placing their shapes, students explained their thinking to others in the group. After some disagreement, they settled on their representation (as shown in fig. 1.13c) and gave two new names to a square, identifying it as a special *rhombus* and a special *rectangle*.

The classification process involved many one-loop sessions first and math talks and interactions throughout each classification activity. Other students often clarified their classmates' misunderstandings, with the teachers facilitating the discussions. The Venn diagram model was used frequently in this classroom to illustrate classifications in other content areas as well.

Summarizing Pedagogical Content Knowledge to Support Big Idea 1 through Essential Understandings 1*a* and 1*b*

Teaching the mathematical ideas in this chapter requires specialized knowledge related to the four components presented in the Introduction: learners, curriculum, instructional strategies, and assessment. The four sections that follow summarize some examples of these specialized knowledge bases in relation to Essential Understandings 1*a* and 1*b*. Although we separate these four components to highlight their importance, we also recognize that they are connected and support one another.

Knowledge of learners

Children explore geometry and their spatial world every day; they learn to "know, explore, conquer, in order to live . . . and move" (Freudenthal 1973, p. 403). We know that young children learn by these exploratory experiences. They develop an informal language to communicate their experiences, and learning for a young child often follows developmental trajectories, steps, or paths. A primary characteristic of young children's learning of geometry is its exploratory nature.

The tasks discussed in this chapter take this learning characteristic into account and build on it. These exploratory sorting tasks provide a variety of experiences with different materials and shapes. For example, incorporating three-dimensional shapes that students can touch, trace, draw, and create is essential if young learners are to understand the properties of three-dimensional shapes. Using plastic straws as line segments and threading the straws with pipe cleaners to join them to form shapes allows students to feel the side of a shape and create the point of intersection between the sides directly and physically.

The materials used are not the only distinguishing feature of these tasks. The shapes that students work with are varied and include examples that are not customary, especially among the paper shapes. Young students often overgeneralize from a few commonplace examples and form misconceptions about shape classifications, such as the notion that a square must "sit flat on its bottom to be a good one," or "All hexagons look like the yellow pattern block" (see Cooper's description on p. 16). To counter these misconceptions or overgeneralizations, students need to be introduced to a diverse group of shapes whenever possible. The variety of materials suggested for the first two tasks is an intentional choice because varied experiences are necessary to support students' development of the concepts encompassed in Essential Understandings 1a and 1b.

A second characteristic of young children's learning of geometry is the development of an informal language to communicate understanding. The words used by students convey their classification descriptions as well as their conceptions of the classification process. Some of the children's phrases shared in this chapter (for instance, "fat triangles" to describe triangular prisms or "squashed rectangles" to describe parallelograms) demonstrate students' tendency to link definitions of shapes that they know, such as triangles and rectangles, to descriptive vocabulary that they understand, such as "fat" and "squashed." Many geometric terms can be difficult to understand. The defining attribute for a rectangle is four right, or 90-degree, angles. "Right angle" may be difficult for young learners to understand if "right" is emphasized. Even if they have some understanding of "angle," they may think that if a shape has a "right angle," it also has a "wrong angle" or a "left angle." To avoid this problem, parents and teachers can use the term "square corner" or "special square corner" to indicate a right angle. Because research shows that even young students can identify a square shape as well as a "corner" (Sarama and Clements 2009), "square corner" seems to be a good alternative to "right angle." Students can then use a square corner "detector" (for example, an index card with the vertex highlighted and the rays of the angle outlined) to identify right angles. Later they can use the defining attribute "four square corners" to identify and categorize rectangles. See figure 1.11b, which shows Daniel's use of this idea.

Although many other characteristics of young children's learning of geometry could be discussed, a third characteristic that has particular relevance to this chapter is the progressive development, through stages or levels, of students' thinking about shapes. The National Research Council (2009) synthesized research on this characteristic and suggests that students "move through different levels in thinking as they learn about geometric shapes." The chart in figure 1.14 is based on this work and outlines the developmental steps for children ages 2 to 5.

Using similar indicators, Clements and Sarama (2009, pp. 143–47) outline additional specific trajectories for children ages 6 to 8 and beyond. In more general terms and with no corresponding ages, the commonly cited van Hiele (1986) levels of geometric thinking describe how young children think about shapes (also see Copley [2010]). The van Hiele framework has three levels:

> **Level 0:** Children learn to recognize geometric figures such as squares and circles by their holistic physical appearance. "Looks like" language is predominant.

> **Level 1:** Children begin to learn isolated characteristics or attributes of the forms—for example, a square has four equal sides.

> **Level 2:** Children establish relationships among the attributes of a form— for instance, a square is a rectangle because it has all of a rectangle's properties.

As noted above, these levels or steps are not cemented by age. Instead, the indicator appears to be experience with two- and three-dimensional shapes, their parts, and relationships. Many of the student responses in figures 1.2–1.5 and 1.10–1.13 can be related to specific steps or levels in these progressions. Most of the students whose work appears in this chapter were at step 1, 2, or 3 or level 0 or 1. The second graders who completed task 5 (see fig. 1.13c) exhibited level 2 reasoning in their comments justifying their thinking that a square is a special rectangle as well as a special rhombus.

These three characteristics of young children's learning of geometry—that it (1) grows out of exploratory experiences, (2) depends on the development of informal language, and (3) progresses through developmental levels of object classification—are certainly relevant to the topics of curriculum, instructional strategies, and assessment that follow.

Steps/ages (level of thinking)	Perceive, say, describe/ discuss, and construct objects in 2-D space	Perceive, say, describe/ discuss, and construct objects in 3-D space
Step 1, ages 2 and 3 (thinking visually/ holistically and thinking about parts)	Recognition and informal description (including at least circles and squares and then triangles and rectangles) Shapes by number of sides	See and describe pictures of objects of all sorts. Discriminate between 2-D and 3-D shapes intuitively, marked by accurate matching or naming.
Step 2, age 4 (thinking visually/ holistically and thinking about parts and relating parts and wholes)	Recognition and informal description, multiple orientations, sizes, and shapes Describe and name shapes by number of sides. Describe and name shapes by number of corners (vertices). Sides of same or different lengths. Right vs. non-right angles.	Describe the difference between 2-D and 3-D shapes and name common 3-D shapes informally and with mathematical names. Identify faces of 3-D objects as 2-D shapes and name those shapes. Informally describe why some blocks "stack well" and others do not.
Step 3, age 5 (thinking visually/ holistically and thinking about parts and relating parts and wholes)	Recognition and informal descriptions, varying orientations, sizes, shapes Shape by number of sides and corners Measure of sides (simple units), gross comparison of angle sizes	Name common 3-D shapes with mathematical terms. Begin to use relational language of "right" and "left." Describe congruent faces and, in context (e.g., block building) parallel faces of blocks.

Fig. 1.14. Steps in the development of young learners' (ages 2–5) "thinking about shapes." From National Research Council (2009, pp. 177–79, 186–87).

Knowledge of curriculum

Historically, geometry was one of the first areas of mathematics taught to young children (Balfanz 1999). Friedrich Froebel, sometimes called "the father of kindergarten," designed a curriculum in the 1850s based on geometric forms and their manipulation in space. (See Chapter 2 for an activity adapted from Froebel's work with kindergartners.) Unfortunately, geometry plays only a minor part in the prekindergarten–grade 2 curriculum today. Most standards, including the Common Core State Standards for Mathematics and other standards provided by state or local educational systems, emphasize number and operations, and they limit their attention to the classification of shapes to having students reason about their properties or attributes throughout the geometry content. Textbooks mirror the emphasis on number and operations, with few topics devoted to geometry. In addition, the manipulation of physical shapes is not feasible with a typical textbook program. Two- and three-dimensional shapes may receive attention only through pictures on a book page, or in rare cases, in a curriculum with virtual manipulatives and technology programs. If students have few manipulatives or little access to technology, they will not have the many and varied experiences that they need to explore shapes and their classifications.

The information in this chapter and its relationship to the curriculum that you use are important for you to consider. Think about your curriculum (including textbooks, materials, and technology) and how it supports, or can be strengthened to support, the development of Essential Understandings 1a and 1b related to classification. Consider and evaluate how your curriculum emphasizes these essential understandings and decide whether you need (1) to continue to use all or part of it, (2) to adapt some of the tasks so they emphasize a different approach, or (3) to create new tasks to address the understandings. Ask yourself questions such as the following:

- How are students introduced to different shape classifications?

- How do the lessons in the curricular materials help students build their understanding?

- Do students have opportunities to use their own language to describe shapes? How are their words connected with more formal classification language?

- Are examples and non-examples of shape classifications addressed in the curriculum?

- Are students introduced to the defining attributes of shape classifications?

- What opportunities do students have to explore, manipulate, and reason about both two- and three-dimensional shapes?

Knowledge of instructional strategies

Teachers can draw on a wide range of instructional strategies to help their students understand the classification of objects. This chapter has illustrated three important instructional strategies: (1) making explicit connections to develop students' conceptual understanding of shape classifications, (2) asking questions to scaffold learning and extend students' understanding, and (3) developing and offering tasks that require thinking.

People understand something if they see how it is related or connected to other things that they know (Hiebert 2003). This connection is especially important to establish between the informal language that young students use and the formal language required for geometric terms to classify two- and three-dimensional shapes. Language like the following helps young students make this connection:

- "Yes, that shape looks like a ball . . . You could call it a *sphere* because it rolls too!"

- "You're right . . . That shape looks like a squashed rectangle, and you called it a *quadrilateral* because it has four sides. Good thinking! Let's look at the straw shape again and see whether every quadrilateral would have the shape of a squashed rectangle."

Or when a student shows that he recognizes a basic characteristic of a triangle by touching a side and saying "three," you can connect additional words with his word and action by inquiring, "Do you mean the number of sides or the number of corners?" (see Amanda's work in fig. 1.2b and her dialogue with her teacher). It is important that these connections be explicit so that students can see how their ideas directly relate to the more formal language.

Questioning is another instructional strategy that can be used effectively to extend students' understanding. The questions need to be specific to the situation and the learner so that students can build their understanding on what others have said. The creation of the Venn diagram shown in figure 1.13c would provide the teacher with an excellent opportunity to explore this type of questioning. The squares in the overlapping loops were the last shapes that the students placed in the diagram. In fact, the loops were not even overlapped initially. The activity began with students in the group selecting one and only one shape. The two loops were labeled "rectangle" and "rhombus," and the students reviewed the definitions of these two shapes. Then the teacher called on the students one at a time to tell where they intended to place their shape and to offer a justification for their selection. The other students were encouraged to agree or disagree with the placement, and the teacher continued to ask questions to help the students to clarify their understanding of each placement. The important scaffolding occurred in the ordering of the objects' placements. First, the teacher called on students who had rhombi that were *not* squares. Second, she called on students who had rectangles that were *not* squares. Third, she called on students who had shapes that were *neither* rhombi *nor* rectangles. Then, finally, she called on students who had squares. In this way, students could experience the progression of thinking, the necessity of overlapping the loops, and the process of clarifying and refining the different ways in which the shapes could be classified.

Developing meaningful tasks that extend students' thinking is an instructional strategy that should underlie every lesson that has a goal of developing essential understanding. The suggested questions and comments on page 38 correlate with excellent tasks that can be added to extend students' thinking. When students are asked to review another student's grouping of objects and decide how these objects were classified, they must recognize similarities and differences between the groups and then label each group with a classification term. Or when students are asked to use only words to explain to someone else how to create a particular shape, they must think of the parts of that shape and a sequence of steps to take to make it and then use their words carefully and thoughtfully to communicate the process.

Knowledge of assessment

As noted in the Introduction, Wiliam (2007) emphasizes the importance of selecting tasks that provide opportunities for students to demonstrate their thinking and for teachers to make instructional decisions. Observation is often the primary assessment technique for use with early learners and is especially important in assessing students' work on classification tasks. Watching how quickly students group objects and their reactions to others' classifications, or taking note of the consistency of their final classifications, can inform instruction as well as a later evaluation of that understanding. The work that students generated in response to the tasks presented in this chapter provided evidence of their understanding or misunderstanding of geometric classification.

A task like the circle-the-rectangles activity in task 3 (fig. 1.7), which yields student responses like those in figure 1.11, can provide teachers with information about their students' ability to give correct or incorrect responses as well as opportunities to have the students explain their reasoning. In most cases, teachers will need to amplify young students' explanations by asking follow-up questions or increasing wait time—or advancing an absurd explanation that will entice students to clarify or extend their response. Note that expressing confusion is a valuable strategy that sometimes elicits more extensive, improved explanations from young children. In fact, a high compliment on the teacher's skillful use of this strategy might take the form of a comment such as the following, offered by a young student to the author: "Teacher, you have so many problems. Come by next year, and we will be happy to help!" No matter what strategies teachers use, they should be sure that assessment occurs before, during, and after instruction so that they may make important instructional decisions as they work with their students.

Conclusion

Classifying two- and three-dimensional shapes is a complex activity. It requires students to recognize similarities and differences among shapes, to use language that helps them communicate about these similarities and differences, to group shapes flexibly so that they can be classified in different ways, and to define shapes by using precise mathematical language. This chapter has presented tasks that help students develop these skills, along with sample responses to these tasks from students. Embedded in these tasks and responses are instructional strategies that teachers can use to help students develop Essential Understandings 1a and 1b and the overarching concept in Big Idea 1 of geometry and measurement: "A classification scheme specifies for a space or the objects within it the properties that are relevant to particular goals and intentions."

Geometry is the study of shape and space. The next chapter expands from shape to space, moving from Big Idea 1 to Big Idea 2: "Geometry allows us to structure spaces and specify locations within them." The topic of space encompasses essential understandings required to identify the location of shapes within structures of space.

practice

Chapter 2
Structuring Space and
Identifying Location

Big Idea 2
Geometry allows us to structure spaces and specify locations within them.

Essential Understanding 2*a*
To describe a location, we must provide a reference point (an origin) and independent pieces of information (often called *coordinates*) indicating distance and direction from that point.

Essential Understanding 2*b*
Geometry and measurement can specify directions, routes, and locations in the world—for example, navigation paths and spatial relations—with precision. Given a reference point and an orientation, we can label positions with numbers.

Essential Understanding 2*c*
Geometric objects are things that exist in our minds. Many of them are idealizations of things that also exist in the physical world.

Geometry involves both shape and space. Unlike students' understanding of shape, their spatial understanding is not a common focus in early childhood mathematics, prompting many to conclude that we have a very narrow view of early childhood and spatial sense. This lack of emphasis is surprising in light of what we observe in young children. They explore geometry and their spatial world every day—they learn to "know, explore, conquer, in order to live . . . and move" (Freudenthal 1973, p. 403).

Working toward Big Idea 2 through Essential Understandings 2a, 2b, and 2c

Children's first teachers intuitively use position words even before children begin to talk. Teachers guide their young students' explorations with phrases like "*inside* the basket," or "*under* your chair" or "*on top of* the box." Or they give directions, asking children to "look *in* the bottom drawer" or "*in front of* the desk" or "*behind* the toy box" to find a lost toy or a missing book—and children learn these directional or positional terms and search diligently for objects in their spatial worlds.

In *Developing Essential Understanding of Geometry and Measurement for Teaching Mathematics in Prekindergarten–Grade 2*, Goldenberg and Clements (2014) isolate and discuss three fundamental concepts, Essential Understandings 2a, 2b, and 2c, which are necessary for students to expand these general descriptions to specify locations and distances in space with precision. These three concepts are embedded in the overarching idea that Goldenberg and Clements present as Big Idea 2—the notion that geometry enables us to structure spaces and specify locations in them. First, students must on some level recognize that specifying the location of an object and the distance to it requires identifying a beginning reference point, the direction of the object from that point in two or three dimensions, the distance of the object from the point of reference, and the orientation of that object (Essential Understanding 2a). Second, they must recognize on some level that measurement helps to describe the distances between objects and between location points (Essential Understanding 2b); Chapter 4 provides more detail about the measurement connection. Third, they need to be able to identify "idealized" objects—abstract geometric shapes—in their environment to help them describe an object's location in space (Essential Understanding 2c). Goldenberg and Clements conclude that these understandings provide an essential foundation for students' later work in three-dimensional space and with latitude and longitude designations.

The focus of this chapter is on tasks that require students to structure space and identify the location of objects within that space. These are presented as tasks 6–8, continuing the numbering from Chapter 1. Specifically, task 6 requires students to locate (find or place) objects—two- or three-dimensional shapes or counters, for instance—by using specific spatial clues—for example, position or shape words, or placement on a number line or on grids of various dimensions. Task 7 asks students to hide objects or shapes and then describe their locations by using spatial clues. Task 8 extends students' work on these tasks to include making simple maps that answer four questions regarding (1) direction, (2) distance (simplified), (3) location, and (4) the identification of objects located on the map.

Task 6: Locating objects in response to verbal clues

Figure 2.1 presents task 6. Examine its five location subtasks, (a)–(e), and respond to the questions about these in Reflect 2.1. These subtasks require students to have an understanding of position and shape words, give attention to clues, and be persistent in placing or finding the object or objects. In most of the subtasks in task 6, *locate* is used to mean *place* rather than *find*—students are asked to place objects as indicated in clues. Reflect 2.1 asks you to consider how the objects to be located in these subtasks, the types of clues that are given, the child's previous experiences, and the location contexts might contribute to differences in the children's responses and understanding.

Reflect 2.1

- **How are the five subtasks different from one another? What specific aspects of the essential understandings does each of them address?**

- **What would a student need to know to complete each of these subtasks successfully?**

All five subtasks in task 6 require students to listen to the spatial clues, eliminate some locations on the basis of the clues, and place (or, in some contexts, find) a particular object or objects. The subtasks differ in three ways: (1) the number and type of objects that they ask students to locate, (2) their use or non-use of idealized shapes in the environment, and (3) their use or non-use of numbers to identify the location in a two- or three-dimensional context.

Subtask 6a asks students only to identify two- or three-dimensional shapes or solids—idealized or actual—and the relative position of an object with respect to those shapes or solids. Note that the sample clues give no direction, distance, or origin, and thus a student uses no numbers to identify the location in a two- or three-dimensional context. Students simply use clues to place an object in a specified relationship with the given shapes or solids. This task can be presented with actual shapes or solids (for example, an orange cube), or it can be offered with idealized shapes that students have identified previously in their environments. (Teachers of prekindergarten and kindergarten often engage their students in labeling a few "idealized" shapes in their school. For instance, they might label a keyhole disk or a screw head as a circle by sticking an adhesive dot on it or identify the classroom door or the front of a fire extinguisher cabinet as a rectangle by attaching to it a small rectangle made with a sticky note.)

Find or place the object or objects identified in each subtask, (a)–(e), below.

Locate _____ by using the spatial clues given:

a.   An object by using 2-D or 3-D shapes and position words

Sample:

Place the hippo

Clue: On top of the orange cube

b.   An object hidden under ten cups in a number line

Sample clue: The bear is hidden under a cup *between* cup 3 and cup 8.

c.   An object hidden on a multicolored 5 × 5 grid (shown here in gray scale)

[red]

[green]

[orange]

[blue]

[purple]

Sample clue: The counter is in the orange row, in the third square.

Fig. 2.1. Task 6

d.   Five objects in a horizontal, vertical, or diagonal line on a 5 × 5 grid

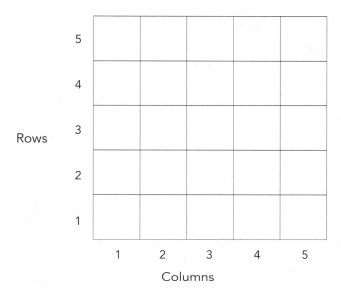

Sample clues: One penguin is in row 3 and column 4. Another penguin is in row 2 and column 4.

e.   Three 2-D or 3-D colored shapes on a grid of rows and columns. Trace the shapes, and color the squares within the outlines to match the color of the shape.

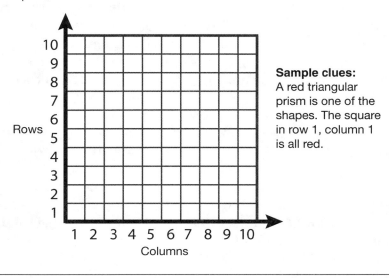

Sample clues:
A red triangular prism is one of the shapes. The square in row 1, column 1 is all red.

Fig. 2.1. *Continued*

Subtask 6b asks students to locate–*find*, this time, rather than *place*–a hidden object in the one-dimensional context of a number line. In this case, the number line is composed of equally spaced plastic cups, turned upside down and labeled with numerals in order. Clues indicate the direction of the location (for example, "before cup 4" or "after cup 9"), and the distance is represented by the sequential order of the numbers written on the cups. (Teachers may say, for instance, "Cup 3 is before cup 4 by just one cup," or "There are many cups after cup 4; cup 5 is closest, and cup 10 is farthest away.") The numbers are used in sequence, and 1 is assumed to be the origin because there is no cup before it.

Subtask 6c provides a beginning two-dimensional context in which students place just one object in one square on a multicolored 5 × 5 grid, with each row a different color. (Note that the colors show only as gray-scale tones in the subtask in fig. 2.1.) Because colors are typically an easy beginning identifier for young children, color clues are given for the rows, and the squares in the rows are identified from left to right by either ordinal numbers–first, second, third, and so forth–or cardinal numbers assigned to the squares–square 1, square 2, square 3, and so on. The given reference point is a row of a particular color, and the numbering of the square begins with 1 on the left and increases left to right in the same manner as in conventional written text and on the number line.

Subtask 6d requires students to place five objects in a line on a 5 × 5 grid in response to clues. Each line on the grid can hold exactly five objects that occupy all the squares in one row, in one column, or on one of the grid's two diagonals–either from the top left corner to the bottom right corner or from the top right corner to the bottom left corner. The location clues can use the two dimensions of the rows and columns. The row and column numbers on the grid imply distance, direction, and an origin. Note that the starting number for the rows is at the bottom of the grid (an orientation similar to coordinate graphs that students will encounter in the upper grades).

In subtask 6e, the students' goal is to use clues that the teacher gives to replicate the grid that she has made beforehand. Before beginning the task with her students, the teacher places three-dimensional shapes on a 10 × 10 grid with numbered rows and columns. Then she traces the outline of the face of each shape on the grid and colors within the outline to match the color of the shape. She is then ready to work with her students, who have their own 10 × 10 grids with rows and columns numbered in the same way. The teacher then gives clues that identify specific squares by providing numbers that indicate a row and a column and the color of the square. With respect to color, the clues indicate whether the square is entirely colored, partially colored, or not colored at all–in other words, is empty. After the teacher has given ten clues, students can request specific clues for specific locations. For example, they might ask, "What is in row 9, column 4?" Success on this task requires knowledge of common solids, the possible faces that could be traced from the solid onto the grid, and the position and orientation of the three-dimensional shape on the grid. For example, figure 2.2 shows the different possibilities for a right triangular prism. Note that this task requires teachers to give many clues for students to identify and place the three different shapes. Students need to work together and identify possible strategies to solve this location task.

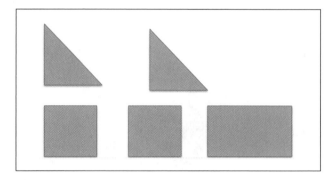

Fig. 2.2. The faces of a triangular prism

Figures 2.3–2.6 and the discussion below detail students' responses to each of these five subtasks. Reflect 2.2 provides questions to guide your examination of these sample responses and help you consider how the teacher might respond to expand students' understanding.

Reflect 2.2

- Examine the students' responses to the five subtasks, (a)–(e), in task 6, as shown in figures 2.3–2.6 and discussed below. Take a few minutes to assess the students' understanding of locating shapes in space. What observations would you make about their understanding?

- What questions would you ask, activities would you encourage, or comments would you make to expand these students' understanding?

Figure 2.3 presents the work of three four-year-olds—Mariah, Mark, and Andrea—on subtask 6a. The students were given a hippo figurine and a collection of red and yellow cubes and cylinders. (The red solids appear as darker, and the yellow solids as lighter, in the black-and-white images in the figure.) The students were given a clue to help them place the hippo accurately: "Locate the hippo between four red cubes and under two yellow cubes." The shapes were not from the environment; rather, they were traditional shapes that students had already explored and classified as "cubes that look like boxes" and "cylinders that look like cans." Thus, the students had already associated them with objects in their everyday environment. It is also important to note that the students were given the clue two times in its entirety, and then, if they asked, it was repeated, either as a whole or broken down into steps. If students have difficulty with this task, the clue should be given one step at a time to see whether the difficulty is with spatial reasoning or with processing multiple steps.

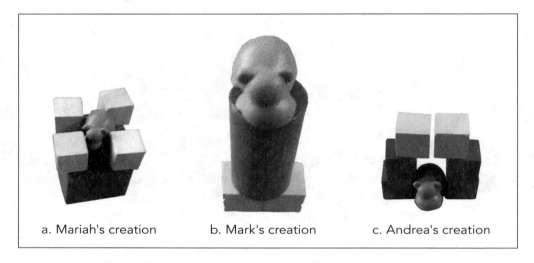

a. Mariah's creation   b. Mark's creation   c. Andrea's creation

Fig. 2.3. Three four-year-olds' responses to subtask 6a

It appears that Mariah (see fig. 2.3a) understood the color words but mixed the numbers (selecting four yellow cubes rather than four red cubes) as well as the position words (placing the hippo between yellow cubes rather than between red cubes, and *on top of* rather than *under*), although she correctly used cubes rather than cylinders. Mark (fig. 2.3b) appears to have understood only that he was to put the hippo somewhere close to shapes and that the shapes were to be both red and yellow. Of the three students, Andrea (fig. 2.3c) exhibited the best understanding of the position language. Positioning the four red cubes took her the most time, and she rearranged them three times before she was satisfied with her creation.

In another activity of this type, students worked together as a class to *find* (rather than *place*) a hippo puppet that their teacher had hidden in the classroom. The teacher gave them four clues with each one leading the students to the next and using idealized shapes:

- Clue 1: The second clue is UNDER a [the clock in the classroom].

- Clue 2: The third clue is INSIDE a [the box holding the blocks in the block center].

- Clue 3: The fourth clue is OVER a [the easel in the teacher center].

- Clue 4: The hippo is ON TOP OF a [the teacher's cupboard].

The students considered the search for the puppet to be a treasure hunt. Each week, the teacher added a new puppet to their story center, and students in the class were selected for the weekend duty of taking care of the new puppet. Some searches continued off and on throughout the day (the triangle formed by the easel proved to be difficult for the students to find, for example); other discoveries were made quickly (for instance, the students easily identified the face of the clock as a circle). Eric Carle's *The Secret Birthday Message* (1986) is an excellent picture book that models this activity, using idealized shapes from the environment.

In subtask 6b, students use clues to find a small object hidden under one cup in a line of cups numbered 1–10. In one prekindergarten class, the teacher hid a bear figurine under cup 6 and gave her students clues to help them find it. The following is an excerpt from a teacher-led discussion with a group of three students in the class—Scott, Lindy, and Todd—who were trying to find the bear:

Teacher: What cup would you like to choose?

Scott: [*Pointing to cup 4*] That's my favorite number! It's 4!

Teacher: [*Turning over cup 4 and leaving it turned*] The bear's not there! It's *after* cup 4 [*gesturing with her hand from 5 to 10*].

Lindy: [*Slowly responding and pointing to cup 1*] It's under the 1!

Teacher: [*Turns over cup 1 and leaves it turned*]

Scott: It can't be there, 'cause it's. . . . [*Waves his hand in a manner similar to the teacher's*]

Todd: I know . . . 9!

Teacher: Show me the cup you mean, Todd. [*Todd identifies cup 9 correctly.*] Here's another clue. It is *before* cup 9 [*again gesturing to the cups that are after cup 4 and before cup 9*]. It is *between* cup 4 and cup 9 [*uses two hands to show the 4 and 9 boundaries*].

Scott: It's 5!

Teacher: Why do you think so?

Scott:	'Cause it's there [*pointing to cup 5*].
Teacher:	[*Turns over cup 5 and leaves it turned*] The bear's not there. Here's another clue . . . It's *after* cup 5 and *before* cup 9. It's *between* 5 and 9.
Lindy:	6!
Teacher:	[*Turns over cup 6*] The bear is under cup 6! Could it have been anywhere else? Why do you think so?
Todd:	Yeah . . . 7 or 8 . . . But she was lucky . . .
Teacher:	Yes, she made a good guess. What would a bad guess have been?

[*Students respond with many answers, including numbers outside the upper boundary and numbers already guessed.*]

Despite the visual and physical clues that the teacher provided, Lindy (as well as other students who appeared to agree) selected a number that did not fit the clues. Scott explained why Lindy's solution wouldn't work; he also made a motion to show a range of possible locations where it could be, just as the teacher had done. Todd appeared to have grasped the importance of a lucky guess (cup 6) among the possibilities indicated by the clues (cups 6, 7, and 8). The teacher's final question addressed the idea of a guess that was "good" and a guess that was "bad." She asked students to give examples of bad guesses—a question that is an excellent way to assess students' understanding of spatial clues related to a number line.

Subtask 6c presents students with a 5 × 5 grid with different-colored rows and gives them clues to place a counter in one particular square in the grid. Figure 2.4 shows the responses of two students, Stephanie (second grade) and Levi (first grade), who were given the following clues:

1. The counter is *not* in the red row. [row 1]

2. The counter is *not* in the purple row. [row 5]

3. The counter is *not* in the orange row. [row 3]

4. The counter is *not* in the green row. [row 2]

5. The counter is in the FIFTH square in the row.

Stephanie's and Levi's work indicates that both students focused on only one aspect of the grid—in Stephanie's case, the rows, and in Levi's, the columns. Stephanie's crossing off of squares in the rows that the clues eliminated was a good strategy for narrowing down the location of the counter, and her use of this technique suggests that she had prior experience with this type of problem. However, Stephanie did not locate the counter correctly in the fifth square in the remaining row. Instead, she placed three counters in squares 2–4. Before Levi placed the counters, he

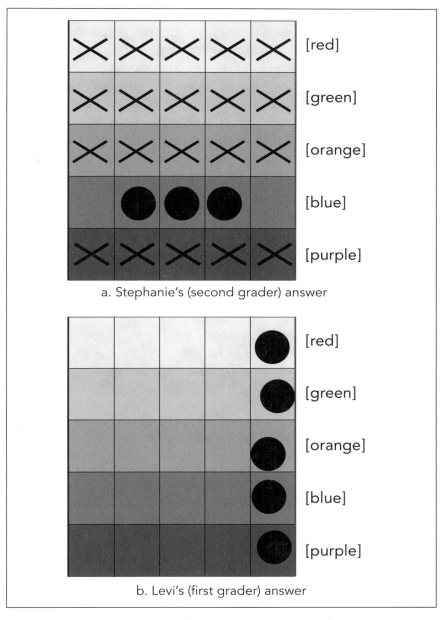

a. Stephanie's (second grader) answer

b. Levi's (first grader) answer

Fig. 2.4. Two students' responses to subtask 6c

asked, "Is the fifth square 5?" In contrast to Stephanie, Levi focused on the position of the object in the correct column—the fifth column—but he seemed to ignore the fact that the clues eliminated rows of certain colors. The teacher might have been able to move Levi forward in his thinking by emphasizing the concept of *not*, along with strategies to help him remember which locations to eliminate from consideration.

Subtask 6d presents a simplified version of a coordinate graphing activity. Students are given clues to place five objects in a line on a 5 × 5 grid with numbered rows and columns. In one first-grade class, students worked in groups of three, with one student placing the five objects on her copy of the grid, shielding it from the view of the other two students, and giving them clues to use to mark their own copies of the grid as they asked questions and made guesses about the location of the objects. Joey, Chet, and Wayne were three students who worked together in the class. Joey placed the objects and gave the clues to the others. He decided that the objects would fill row 5 on the grid. Chet and Wayne asked questions and made guesses about the location of the objects. The following dialogue developed among the three students as they worked:

> *Chet:*   I guess row 2, column 3.
>
> *Joey:*   No!
>
> [*Chet marks row 2, column 3, with an X on his grid.*]
>
> *Wayne:*   I guess row 4, column 4.
>
> *Joey:*   No!
>
> [*Wayne marks his grid incorrectly, placing an X in row 5, column 4. Chet explains his mistake, showing Wayne the square he should have marked, row 4, column 4. Wayne gets a new grid and re-marks it correctly.*]
>
> *Chet:*   I guess row 5, column 1.
>
> *Joey:*   Yes.
>
> *Chet:*   [*Whispers to Wayne*] Guess row 5, column 2.
>
> *Wayne:*   OK. Row 5, column 2.
>
> *Joey:*   Yes!
>
> [*Chet is visibly excited and gives a thumbs-up. Wayne colors in his square but his actions do not indicate that he knows the solution.*]
>
> *Chet:*   Yeah! We know! We can color in the whole row!
>
> [*While Chet colors in the entire row, Wayne watches.*]
>
> *Wayne:*   I want to keep guessing. Why are you coloring those [*pointing to the other squares*]?
>
> *Chet:*   'Cause it is a row. It's the only thing it can be! [*Goes on to show and explain all the rows it cannot be.*]
>
> [*Wayne is still unsure, and although he colors in the remaining squares to match Chet's grid, he acts as though he doesn't understand.*]

Figure 2.5 shows the grids of the three students, with Wayne's and Chet's at the top and Joey's at the bottom.

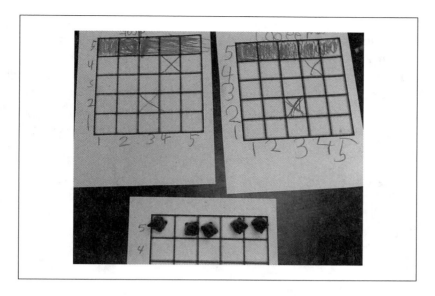

Fig. 2.5. Responses from a group of three first-grade students to subtask 6d

As the dialogue among the three students indicates, only four guesses were necessary for Chet and Wayne to find the objects that Joey had placed. The two first-grade guessers interacted with each other, one helping the other place an X correctly and also explaining why they needed only four guesses to find the solution. Chet seems to have easily grasped the grid's location clues and the logic that produces the quickest answer. By contrast, it appears that Wayne would need more location experiences with this type of grid and might need to play the game over and over again with the same rules to give time for Chet's reasoning to make sense to him and for his own reasoning to develop more fully. Joey also appeared surprised by Chet's reasoning, which he didn't seem to understand, expressing the idea that the boys had been "lucky."

As expected, subtask 6e was the most challenging of the location tasks. Before approaching this activity, students should have gained familiarity with triangular and rectangular prisms through hands-on experiences with colored blocks and should have identified and traced the prism's faces on grid paper. In one class of twenty-five second graders, the teacher traced the rectangular face of a red triangular prism, the triangular face of a blue triangular prism, and the square face of an orange cube on the grid. Students worked in groups and used the teacher's clues to color in squares on their grids, and then they predicted what solids could have been used to make the outlines. The next day, students posed questions about the colors of particular squares on the grid. After the teacher responded, the students continued to make predictions. This second-grade class worked on the task for three days, and the students' responses illustrate the importance of the role that experience plays in learning. Many students suggested that this activity was "like Battleship," a game that some had played on the computer or as a board game. Others had never experienced a positional game like this. Some students were familiar with two-dimensional grids and used their experiences to help others in their group. Figure 2.6 shows several students' grids as they collected data from the clues. The outlines in the lower photo show their conjectures about the location of the shapes. The colored and crossed-off squares show their responses to the clues (colors appear in the figure as shades of gray).

Students who were the most successful with this task appeared to share a number of characteristics. They were able to (1) correctly eliminate the squares that did not

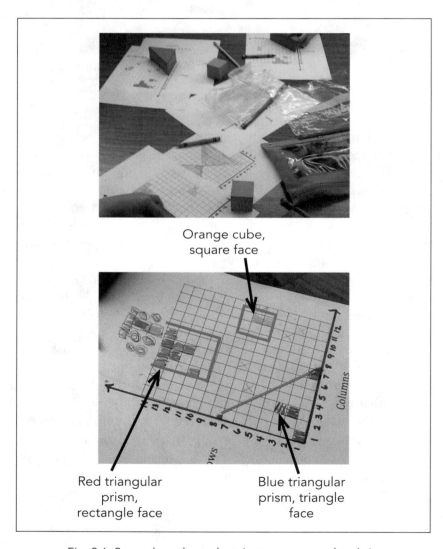

Fig. 2.6. Second-grade students' responses to subtask 6e

have the correct color and mark those squares with an X, (2) consider the differences among the shapes made by specific faces of the three-dimensional shape, (3) interact with their peers to solve the problem, and (4) persist as they correctly recorded the data and used it to make their conjectures.

Task 7: Hiding objects and describing their locations to others

Task 7, shown in figure 2.7, presents a set of subtasks whose contexts are similar to those in task 6, but this time all the objects are hidden. The notion that precise language is important to specify locations within structured spaces is part of Big Idea 2 and is especially evident in Essential Understanding 2a, which highlights the precise language on which "a reference point and independent pieces of information (often called *coordinates*)" depend when they "indicate distance and direction from that point."

Hide _____. Tell how to find _____ by using your words as clues.

  a. An object in relation to 2-D or 3-D shapes by using position words

  b. An object hidden under ten cups in a line

  c. An object hidden on a 5 × 5 grid

  d. Five objects in a horizontal, vertical, or diagonal row on a 5 × 5 grid

  e. Five 2-D shapes on a grid of rows and columns

  f. Three 3-D shapes on a grid of rows and columns

Fig. 2.7. Task 7

Reflect 2.3 asks you to consider what you would expect students to include in descriptions of the locations of hidden objects. Review the contexts used in tasks 6 and 7. Think about how you could encourage more precise language.

Reflect 2.3

- What spatial words or phrases would you expect students to use to describe the locations of objects (perhaps their own creations) that they have hidden on a one-dimensional number line or a two-dimensional grid?

- How could you prompt students to be more precise in their descriptions? What questions could you ask? What comments could you make? What activities could you offer?

Students' descriptions of the locations of objects that they have hidden often include phrases that they have heard teachers or their peers use in situations like those in the subtasks in the previous task, task 6. To encourage more precise language, you might use the following questions, comments, or activities:

- **Questions concerning reference points and coordinates:**
  - [*If clues are sequential*] "Where should I begin if I want to find the first clue?"
  - "When I count the rows on the grid, where is row 1? Where is row 5?"
  - "Where does the number line begin?"
  - "Where is the first column located on the grid?"
  - "What two numbers could you use to describe the location of the _____ square on the grid?"
  - "What direction should I go in to find the _____?"
  - "How far should the _____ be from the purple row?"

- **Comments concerning the location of the hidden objects:**
  - "From your clues, I think the _____ could be behind the rectangular prism *or* under a rectangle."
  - "Please tell me more about where the _____ is so I can find it."
  - "I know the row that the _____ is in. I just need to know the column."

- **Activities that encourage the use of precise language:**
  - Play a matching game in which two students have exactly the same number and type of objects and the same context (a grid or a number line, for example). One student, working out of view of the other, places her objects in the context. Then she describes the objects' placement to the other student, who tries to place his objects in the context to match her description. The two students then compare their placements to check the accuracy of his placement and refine the precision of her description.
  - Ask students to work as a class to mount their shape creations in an array, and display the large rectangular array somewhere in the classroom. Then have students use words to describe exactly where their own creation is located in the large array. (Note that this activity is particularly effective for parent open-house events. Be sure that students describe their particular creation with words only and without actions, and have parents try to locate their children's creations in the classroom.)

Figure 2.8 shows a rectangular array on the wall in a prekindergarten classroom. Students' individual creations were made by covering a 12-inch by 18-inch sheet of newsprint with a variety of rectangular shapes. Each student described his or her creation by telling where it was located in the array and the size and color of the rectangles in it. A four-year-old offered the following description to help a parent locate her creation (outlined in black in the figure) in the array:

Child: My rectangle has lots of rectangles, an orange square, and lots of green, black, and red rectangles. It is on the bottom of the board and kind of in the middle.

Parent: Why do you have an orange square? I thought this was supposed to be a rectangle.

Child: 'Cause my teacher said squares are special rectangles. I don't know why!

Fig. 2.8. A rectangular array of prekindergartners' 12-inch by 18-inch creations, with one student's work outlined

A 2 × 2 array of grids with designs formed by using wooden circles or parts of circles appears in figure 2.9. These creations were based on materials from Friedrich Froebel's gift 8, "Sticks and Rings." In the geometry curriculum that Froebel designed for young children in the 1850s, he called the sequential materials "gifts," and children were expected to explore three-dimensional shapes first before progressing to two-dimensional shapes, then lines, and then points. The four kindergarten and first-grade students who made the array shown in the figure described the locations of their own designs by using the design's placement in the array as well as the positions of the circles or circle parts on the grid. These four students described their creations in the following ways:

- "My picture has circles that make yellow [and] white patterns. It is in the top row on that side" [*motioning to the left side*].

- "My picture is in the bottom row, and it starts five rows down from the top."

- "My picture is on the bottom row too, and it has five big circles with five little circles inside the others. It also has two circles that are just part of a circle."

- "My circles have blue red circle patterns and red white patterns. It is on the right side and on the top row."

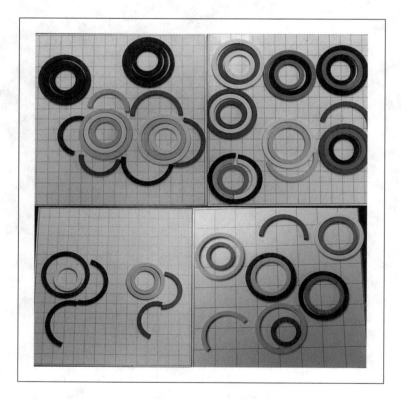

Fig. 2.9. A 2 × 2 array of grids showing kindergartners' and first graders' wooden circle creations

Note that in the examples shown in figures 2.8 and 2.9, the students actually created grids by arranging their individual creations in an array. These types of grids complement the more formal grids used in tasks such as subtasks 6c, 6d, and 6e and provide descriptions of "independent pieces of information" as expressed in Essential Understanding 2*a*.

Task 8: Representing real-world locations with maps

Task 8, shown in figure 2.10, asks students to make a map showing how to get from one point to another, with landmarks labeled with shapes. This task addresses the very important idea, captured in Essential Understanding 2*b*, that we can "specify directions, routes, and locations in the world . . . with precision."

Make a map showing how to go from _____ to _____. Label the landmarks, using shapes.

Make the map for your friend who can't read.

Fig. 2.10. Task 8

Note that this task again presents a location problem, but this time identifying or specifying a location includes the creation of a map—a map that is completely visual and contains enough visual clues that a verbal description is not necessary. In addition, this task is a real-world problem—that is, this task should result in a map that gives directions from one real place to another real place in a young child's world. As Goldenberg and Clements (2014, p. 28) state, "Any work with maps involves four questions:

- Which way? (direction)

- How far? (distance)

- Where? (location)

- What objects? (identification)."

Before reading on, turn to Reflect 2.4, and respond to the questions, which ask you to analyze situations that require a map.

Reflect 2.4

- When might a young child need a map to go from one location to another location?

- How could a young child make a map that would address the four components of work with maps—direction, distance, location, and identification?

Figures 2.11–2.14 show four specific examples of young students' maps: (1) a pre-kindergartner's map of the path that his class took on a field trip to the zoo (fig. 2.11); (2) a story map, created by kindergartners first on the floor with objects from the classroom and then transferred to paper and showing the changes in story contexts (fig. 2.12); (3) a map using labels to organize a new school setting in an early child-hood classroom (fig. 2.13); and (4) a first grader's map showing summer travels (fig. 2.14). Each of these maps is discussed in turn in the paragraphs that follow.

Figure 2.11 shows a map drawn by a four-year-old after he returned from a field trip to the zoo. He drew all the elements of the map and then asked his teachers to write the words on the rectangles that he had made to represent the areas of particular animals. He was very specific about the words that went on each rectangle, and he was in fact correct about the progression, starting in the bottom right-hand corner of the map. This child made a curving path, placed trees throughout the map, and drew a forest in the upper right-hand corner—all correctly. He made his map by his own choice to show what happened at the zoo; the teacher had asked only that members of the class draw a picture showing what they had liked best on their field trip. Note that the map indicates direction by the path, which goes from the right-hand corner around to the other side, shows general distance and location by curved lines separating the rectangle labels, and makes identifications by the animal labels.

Figure 2.12 shows the work of a group of kindergartners in creating a story map that they organized spatially on the floor before recreating it on paper. The students created a story about dinosaurs in the block center (fig. 2.12a). They borrowed dinosaur and people counters from the math center and triangles from the teacher's shape box. The triangles were two colors—blue and green (the green ones are lighter than the blue ones in the black-and-white image). They also worked with blocks in two colors—orange and brown (the orange ones are lighter than the brown ones in the image). When asked, the students said that the orange blocks "go around" the island, the brown blocks make a building on the island, the blue triangles represent the water around the island, and the green triangles represent the jungle for the dinosaurs. The students in this group were quite excited about their created story.

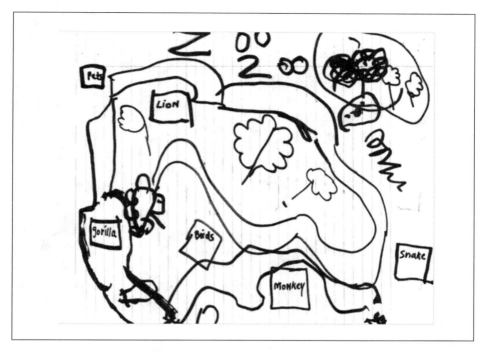

Fig. 2.11. A prekindergartener's map of the path taken on a field trip to the zoo

In interacting with one another, they used many sorts of position words as they described the location of the island, the jungle, the water, and the various animals and people.

When the activity time ended, the teacher explained that the block center needed to be cleaned up and everything put away, and she asked the students to make a story map on paper, showing where the action in their story took place. The students immediately saw the need to record their work so that they could recreate their story another day. In the picture that they created (fig. 2.12b), one student made the jungle at the top, another student made the dinosaurs in the middle of the jungle, and a third student made the city wall (rectangles at the bottom of the drawing) around the island. The lighter (green) "jungle" triangles surrounded the pictures of the dinosaurs, and the darker (blue) "water" triangles surrounded the island. In this first map-making effort, the students showed the location of the dinosaurs and people and identified the parts of the map, but they did not indicate distance or direction. Later, the teacher helped the students write their story and include arrows to show where characters were throughout and indicate other landmarks.

Teachers also make maps of another sort for early learners. Classroom organization and visual reminders of the locations of objects and spaces are important for young

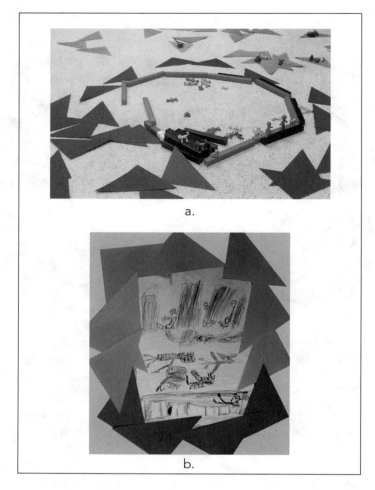

a.

b.

Fig. 2.12. Kindergartners' story map,
(a) on the floor, and (b) transformed into a picture

students, who need to be able to develop independence as well as the ability to locate themselves in relation to the space in the classroom and their school. Mapping locations by using symbols, color coding, arrows, or pathways is important for students as well as adults. Students who know where they are and where they are going in their educational setting will be able to learn and have better opportunities for learning. Distance can be reported by using colored yarn wrapped on a spool or cash register tape marked with a colored pen. Pollman (2010, pp. 9–10) includes a useful story about Mrs. Knapp's classroom, detailing how children in a kindergarten class used landmarks, color labels, and photographs to create a map.

Teachers use a variety of labels and landmarks to help students locate materials for use in learning centers. Figure 2.13 shows different types of labels for materials. The array model in (a) shows rows and columns of tubs containing the same number. The tubs in each row have labels that are a different color. Students are required to complete the tasks contained in a different colored tub each day, and the numbers of dots indicate specific levels of activities (easy, medium, etc.). Note that students need to match (or *subitize*) the number represented by the dot pattern to place the tub in the correct column as well as the correct row.

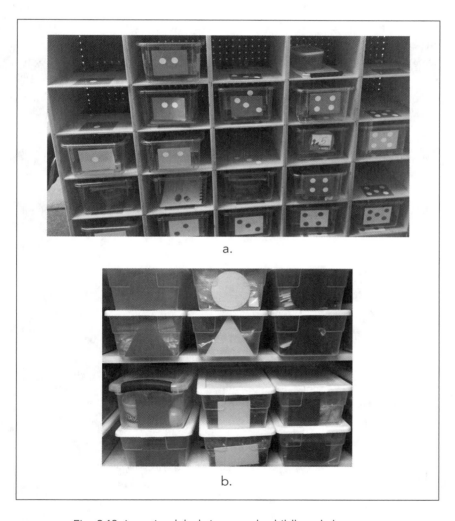

a.

b.

Fig. 2.13. Location labels in an early childhood classroom

The system in part (b) of figure 2.13 is similar to that in part (a) but uses shape as the identifier for each of the columns. In both systems, labels help students use direction, location, and identification to find materials in their classroom. The number sequence of the dot pattern in the rows in the top photograph can be thought of as a number line from 1 to 5 that could be used to explore rudimentary distance indicators—for example, tub 4 is three tubs away from tub 1.

Figure 2.14 illustrates the attention that young students are capable of giving to direction, location, and identification in a map. A first grader, Jack, created the map shown in the figure to describe his travels during the summer. He drew his map several days after his trip without looking at any maps; however, a Google map was displayed on the screen in his car throughout much of his trip. Jack described his trip orally by pointing to each name on his map in order of his visits to the places: Godfrey, Alton, Branson, Oklahoma, Alton, Godfrey, Chicago, and then "Our place." The outlined shapes on the map are Illinois and Missouri and Oklahoma.

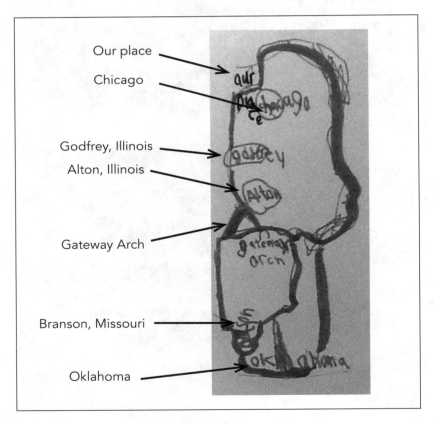

Fig. 2.14. A first grader's map showing
his travels during summer vacation

Notable features of Jack's mapmaking include his use of labels; the partially correct relationship that he represented among the locations of the states of Illinois, Missouri, and Oklahoma; and his generally correct relative positioning of the cities (for example, Godfrey is north of Alton, Chicago is north(east) of Alton, and Branson, Missouri, is north of Oklahoma.

Summarizing Pedagogical Content Knowledge to Support Big Idea 2 through Essential Understandings 2*a*, 2*b*, and 2*c*

Teaching the mathematical ideas in this chapter requires specialized knowledge related to the four components presented in the Introduction: learners, curriculum, instructional strategies, and assessment. The four sections that follow summarize some examples of these specialized knowledge bases in relation to Essential Understandings 2*a*, 2*b*, and 2*c*. Although we separate them to highlight their importance, we also recognize that they are connected and support one another.

Knowledge of learners

As noted at the beginning of this chapter, spatial thinking begins to develop very early as babies explore their environment, move through space, and locate objects that they want. The developmental progression for spatial thinking involves two components: (1) spatial orientation and (2) spatial visualization and imagery. The first of these, spatial orientation, is the focus of this chapter and involves the making and using of maps and coordinates. The second component, spatial visualization and imagery, will be discussed in Chapter 5. On the basis of their research, Clements and Sarama (2009) propose a progression in the development of young children's spatial orientation from birth to age 8. Figure 2.15 shows the outlines of that progression, with each stage matched with student examples from this chapter.

The students whose work appears in this chapter exhibited many of the characteristics linked to stages in this learning progression trajectory. Unfortunately, as the next section indicates, the standard U.S. curriculum for prekindergarten–grade 2 does not emphasize, or even mention, most of the steps on this teaching and learning path.

Knowledge of curriculum

Friedrich Froebel developed a highly spatial program for young children in the 1850s. His "gifts" were tasks that required students to place three-dimensional blocks, two-dimensional shapes (including circles and lines), and points to represent (a) forms of life, (b) forms of knowledge, and (c) forms of beauty. (Froebel

Age	Progression and description	Example
4	**Small local framework user:** Locates objects after movement, even if target is not specified ahead of time. Searches a small area comprehensively, often using a circular search pattern.	Makes map showing the circular arrangement of the animal areas at the zoo (see fig. 2.11). Finds and locates own creation on simplified grid (see fig. 2.8).
5	**Local framework user:** Locates objects after movement, maintaining the overall shape of the arrangement of objects. Represents objects' positions relative to landmarks. Locates objects, using maps with pictorial cues. Can extrapolate two coordinates, understanding their integration to one position, as well as use coordinate labels in simple situations. Some use of coordinate labels in simple situations.	Correctly interprets clues about locations on a simple coordinate grid (see Chet's response to subtask 6d on p. 54 and work in fig. 2.5). Creates story maps to show movements and changes of objects in space (see the kindergartners' story map in fig. 2.12). Describes location of individual work in a 2 × 2 grid (see fig. 2.9 and associated discussion on p. 60).
6	**Map user:** Locates objects by using maps with pictorial cues. Can extrapolate two coordinates, understanding their integration to one position, as well as use coordinate labels in simple situations.	Uses labels in different colors and with different numbers of shapes or dots to organize objects into rows and columns in the classroom (see fig. 2.13 and associated discussion on pp. 65–66).
7	**Coordinate plotter:** Reads and plots coordinates on maps.	Plays positional, Battleship-like games to locate shapes (see discussion of second graders' work on task 6e on pp. 55–57).

Fig. 2.15. Developmental progression for spatial orientation
(Clements and Sarama 2009), paired with age-appropriate examples

had students use grids as backgrounds to complete these tasks.) The wooden circle creations in figure 2.9 are an updated version of Froebel's gift 8, Sticks and Rings.

In the Common Core State Standards for Mathematics, standards involving spatial understanding are specified only for kindergarten, and then the topic is largely ignored in the standards for first and second grade. Although locations and comparisons on a one-dimensional number line are involved in the number standards in all grades, two-dimensional locations with coordinates are not specifically considered until grade 5—specifically, in standards 5.G.1 and 5.G.2, clustered under "Graph points on the coordinate plane to solve real-world and mathematical problems."

It is important that you consider the information in this chapter and how it relates to the curriculum you use. Think about your materials, textbooks, and technology and how they relate to Essential Understandings 2a, 2b, and 2c. Also think about how your state's standards relate to the information in this chapter. If your standards do not emphasize these ideas, how will you decide what you need to do to help students develop their understanding of them? In most cases, to promote the development of your students' spatial orientation, you will need to add some activities and tasks intentionally or provide experiences that will help students grow in this area.

Consider the following questions:

- How can you organize your classroom to make spatial orientation part of the "hidden" curriculum?

- How can you add experiences with grids or coordinate graphs to your materials to encourage your students' attention to two-dimensional location tasks?

- What additional materials do you need to support your students' development of spatial orientation?

- Do materials that you use in other curricular areas (for example, social studies, language arts, or science) promote the development of spatial orientation? If so, do they help to build these mathematical essential understandings? If not, how can you include contexts in other content areas that will develop these understandings?

- What opportunities for mapping does your classroom context offer? Can you find useful real-world examples that you can introduce into your classroom?

Knowledge of instructional strategies

"The research reviewed . . . suggests that development of geometric knowledge is fueled by experience and education, not just maturation" (National Research Council 2009, p. 192). This finding about the importance of experience and education lends strong support for intentional and rich instruction. Teachers can draw on a wide range of instructional strategies to help their students with spatial orientation. This chapter specifically illustrates three instructional strategies:

1. Using real-world examples that connect with a young student's world

2. Taking every opportunity to expand and emphasize spatial orientation

3. Focusing on and encouraging precise descriptive language

The world of a young child is filled with examples that teachers can use to support the development of spatial orientation. Giving students directions that use a variety of spatial terms and waiting patiently for their adherence to them rather than impatiently showing them what to do will help them build their understanding. Or asking students to locate an item by using landmarks and spatial terms rather than finding a missing object yourself or sending someone else to locate it will provide some real-life experiences. Creating and using maps for real-life problems is especially relevant and instructionally productive. In this chapter, some of the sample activities were not initially planned as student activities. Rather, they evolved from observing situations that required remembering where objects had been placed for a story before they had to be returned to the block center (see the story map in fig. 2.12), or situations in which a student constructed a map of his travels during the summer (see fig. 2.14). These kinds of activities and situations, along with many more, abound in classrooms. If we encourage activities that students care about, engaging students in them can only expand their spatial understanding.

Looking for and using opportunities to expand and emphasize spatial orientation are especially important. The essential understandings that support spatial orientation are involved in many other content areas. For example, language and literacy include position words as important vocabulary to interpret a story. Social studies content suggests mapping standards. And science often uses coordinate graphing to organize and display information. The integration of these content areas can help students make connections and increase their spatial understanding. Organizational classroom strategies such as mapping the classroom, marking landmarks, and planning how to travel to the playground or the nurse's office are all critical for making smooth transitions and promoting general classroom order. Structuring the environment so that materials can be easily located is a simple way to expand students' spatial orientation (see fig. 2.13). Containers where students turn in their work can also be labeled by rows and columns—for example, a label might indicate that John's work is to go in row 7, column 2, in the materials box. Games such as Battleship or Where's the Bear? should be played by students for enjoyment as well as to promote spatial understanding.

Encouraging precise descriptive language can be an instructional goal for any essential understanding. However, it is especially important for spatial orientation. Instead of using general terms to describe the location of an object, teachers should model, use, and listen for precise vocabulary (saying, for example, "the right column," rather than "over here," or "in the bottom row, in the third column from the left," rather than "there"). Class jobs can include "direction givers" who welcome new students or visitors to the classroom and use class-created maps to show where materials or centers are located or "message runners" who travel to other areas in the school to deliver communications or materials. Students who do these jobs will need to practice using precise vocabulary in their descriptions.

Knowledge of assessment

Observation is the primary method of assessment for young students' spatial orientation. Watching students as they locate objects in space and move in their environment is a natural activity that can occur almost every day. Listening to class news as students tell where they went over the weekend and asking questions about their trip can also inform your assessment of a student's progress in spatial orientation. In addition, observing students as they solve problems that require finding objects, play games involving spatial orientation, or use classroom structures or maps can provide good assessment data that can inform instruction.

"Follows directions" is often an expectation on report cards for young students. Frequently, teachers and parents report that young students "cannot follow more than one direction at a time," or, put simply, "cannot follow directions." It is important that adults consider a child's development of spatial orientation and how it serves as an indicator of a young student's ability to follow directions. Are students not able to follow directions because they don't understand the spatial language used, or the structure of the environment, or the location landmarks? Or is the problem a hearing difficulty or perhaps a lack of focus on the steps in the directions? Part of the assessment process is identifying the specific reason why students have difficulty with a skill or concept and then changing the environment or the instruction to facilitate learning.

Conclusion

Chapter 2 has discussed an essential concept that is often ignored when young students study geometry—space. Big Idea 2 states, "Geometry allows us to structure spaces and specify locations within them." This chapter has presented three spatial tasks and examined students' responses to them. Task 6, with subtasks (a)–(e), calls on students to locate—find or place—objects in space. Task 7 provides students with opportunities to hide an object and give clues to help someone else find it, thus providing teachers and others with valuable access to students' descriptions of space. Task 8 extends students' experience of organizing and structuring space by asking them to make a simple map. This task involves students in thinking about and deciding how to show at least some of the basic spatial information represented on a map: (1) direction, (2) distance, (3) location, and (4) place names. This chapter has also presented student-created maps and illustrated students' use of simplified questions and answers regarding these elements.

Chapter 3 will consider an essential understanding that is particularly important to future work—both with measurement of geometric attributes (Chapter 4) and with transformation of shapes and objects (Chapter 5). Essential Understanding 4d, the focus of Chapter 3, concerns the usefulness of decomposing and composing objects to measure them. This insight is a facet of Big Idea 4: "One way to analyze geometric objects, relationships among them, or the spaces that they occupy is to quantify—measure or count—one or more of their attributes." Young students need a variety of experiences with decomposing and composing both two- and three-dimensional shapes.

practice

Chapter 3
Decomposing and Composing Shapes

Essential Understanding 4*d*
Objects can be decomposed and composed to facilitate their measurement.

This chapter focuses on just one essential understanding identified by Goldenberg and Clements in *Developing Essential Understanding of Geometry and Measurement for Teaching Mathematics in Prekindergarten–Grade 2* (2014). This is the fundamental concept captured in Essential Understanding 4*d*—that decomposing and composing objects can facilitate their measurement. Because the processes of decomposing and composing both two- and three-dimensional shapes are foundational to the development of other geometric concepts, as well as some concepts dealing with fractions and multiplication, developing this essential understanding from the earliest years is very important.

Working toward Essential Understanding 4*d*

Because we know that an understanding of geometric concepts is "fueled by experience and education, not just maturation" (National Research Council 2009, p. 192), discussing experiences with decomposition and composition of shapes makes a great deal of sense before turning to early experiences with measuring those shapes. Essential Understanding 4*d* has center stage in Chapter 3, but it also plays an important role in Chapter 4, which focuses on measuring geometric attributes of two- and three-dimensional shapes. For example, to determine the area of a two-dimensional shape, one may find it helpful to decompose the shape into other shapes that can be easily measured. Then one may simply add the individual measurements to find the total measurement of the initial shape. Or, to find the surface area of a polyhedron, one might decide that it would make sense to decompose the shape to calculate the area of each face on the surface by using known strategies or formulas. In other words, the activities in Chapter 3 will facilitate the learning of the concepts in Chapter 4. Although all the chapters address different understandings, the activities that they present and discuss do not support discrete, unrelated understandings. Rather, the chapters build on one another, with almost every chapter offering evidence of shape, space, decomposition and composition, measurement, and transformation.

The Common Core State Standards for Mathematics (CCSSM) also emphasize the content of this chapter by setting out two standards at each grade level, K–2, dealing with composing and decomposing of shapes (National Governors Association Center for Best Practices and Council of Chief State School Officers [NGA Center and CCSSO] 2010). These CCSSM standards are shown below, along with the related expectation for prekindergarten articulated in *Curriculum Focal Points for Prekindergarten through Grade 8 Mathematics* (NCTM 2006). Note that both the first- and the second-grade standards in CCSSM deal with decomposition of regular two-dimensional shapes primarily to focus on equal shares and foundational fraction concepts.

> *Prekindergarten* (Curriculum Focal Points and Connections [NCTM 2006, p. 11])
>
> [Children] build pictures and designs by combining two- and three-dimensional shapes.

> *Kindergarten* (Geometry [K.G], CCSSM 2010, p. 12)
>
> **Analyze, compare, create, and compose shapes.**
>
> 5. Model shapes in the world by building shapes from components (e.g., sticks and clay balls) and drawing shapes.
>
> 6. Compose simple shapes to form larger shapes.

> *Grade 1* (Geometry [1.G], CCSSM 2010, p. 16)
>
> **Reason with shapes and their attributes.**
>
> 2. Compose two-dimensional shapes (rectangles, squares, trapezoids, triangles, half-circles, and quarter-circles) or three-dimensional shapes (cubes, right rectangular prisms, right circular cones, and right circular cylinders) to create a composite shape, and compose new shapes from the composite shape.

3. Partition circles and rectangles into two and four equal shares, describe the shares using the words *halves*, *fourths*, and *quarters*, and use the phrases *half of, fourth of,* and *quarter of.* Describe the whole as two or four of the shares. Understand for these examples that decomposing into more equal shares creates smaller shares.

Grade 2 (Geometry [2.G], CCSSM 2010, p. 20)

Reason with shapes and their attributes.

2. Partition a rectangle into rows and columns of same-size squares and count to find the total number of them.

3. Partition circles and rectangles into two, three, or four equal shares, describe the shares using the words *halves, thirds, half of, a third of,* etc., and describe the whole as two halves, three thirds, four fourths. Recognize that equal shares of identical wholes need not have the same shape.

Decomposition and composition with 3–D shapes

Building with three-dimensional shapes is a common activity in prekindergarten and kindergarten classrooms. How can this familiar activity be used intentionally to teach geometric concepts and the decomposition and composition of three-dimensional shapes? Respond to the questions in Reflect 3.1, and think about how you might structure the classroom environment so that students not only experience decomposing and composing three-dimensional shapes but also learn something about their geometric attributes. In addition, consider what you could assess about their understanding from observations as they compose or decompose three-dimensional shapes.

Reflect 3.1

- **How could you facilitate students' understanding of composition and decomposition of three-dimensional shapes in the block center?**

- **How would you assess students' understanding during three-dimensional composition and decomposition activities?**

Observations of students as they work with blocks include many opportunities to take note of characteristics that permit an assessment of students' development—social and emotional as well as cognitive. Using block sets that include more than rectangular prisms of one color can facilitate assessment of students' understanding of three-dimensional shapes and their building capabilities. Three-dimensional shapes should include triangular prisms, square and triangular pyramids, hexagonal prisms, spheres, cones, and cylinders, as well as a variety of rectangular prisms. This variety of shapes gives students opportunities to investigate the attributes that permit rolling, stacking, and sliding, and when a cardboard ramp is added, the number of possible investigations increases.

Many games provide opportunities for assessment. An informal game, "Toss and Build," is just one possibility. Two students take turns tossing a regular die and then selecting that number of three-dimensional blocks. Working together, they use their blocks to build a tower on a colored-paper foundation. When it is their turn, they toss the die and add to the tower. If the tower falls down or a block in the tower falls off, they can try to build again by adding the same number of blocks, or they can choose to remove one block from the remaining tower and then add their blocks. You may be surprised to learn that some students in prekindergarten try to place a sphere at the top or add a triangular prism "so it looks like a roof," making it impossible for the other child to continue to build.

Problems can also be posed for students working in the block center. For example, two kindergartners were discussing "fairness" as they considered which of them had "all the good blocks." A task like the following might build on their discussion and extend their thinking: "Make homes for two people. The only rule is that the two homes must be exactly the same and connected to each other" (in other words, they must be symmetrical). Figure 3.1 shows the different paired houses made by two kindergarten students, Caleb and Cody. Caleb (fig. 3.1a) made a rather typical creation, using five blocks on each side of his structure, for a total of ten blocks. Cody built an amazing construction with colored tangram blocks. Parts (b) and (c) of figure 3.1 show his work from two points of view at the end of thirty minutes.

These two examples highlight the variation in young children's experience with blocks more than differences in their development. As noted earlier, prekindergartners who played "Toss and Build" sometimes chose a sphere to stack in the tower and seemed surprised when it would not stay on the tower. Others placed the triangular prisms in such a way that they stacked well and were frustrated when other students did not understand "the right way to do it!" In a similar way, Cody and Caleb's houses were quite different, even though the two students were the same age and appeared to spend the same amount of time in the block center each day. Again, the finding that students' understanding of geometric concepts is "fueled by experience and education, not just maturation" (National Research Council 2009, p. 192) seems to be relevant to the difference in the complexity of the two examples of student work in figure 3.1.

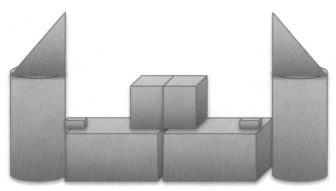

a. Sketch of Caleb's houses

b. Cody's houses, viewed from the front

c. Cody's houses, viewed from above

Fig. 3.1. Symmetrical block houses for two people,
constructed by two kindergartners, Caleb and Cody

Task 9: Architects and builders

Continuing the numbering of tasks from Chapters 1 and 2, the first task in Chapter 3 is task 9. In this two-part task, which appears in figure 3.2, students act first as architects. They make model buildings of their own with 3-D blocks and then draw their creations so that students acting as builders can replicate their structures from their plans. Then the students who were originally architects work with other students' plans, becoming builders who erect other architects' creations from their building plans. Consider the questions in Reflect 3.2 as you view the results of this task as completed by students in prekindergarten–grade 1, shown in figures 3.3–3.5.

Be an architect. Build a model building. Draw your building so that others can build it by using your plan [or a photograph].

Be a builder. Select an architect's plan [or photograph]. Build a building to match the plan. Show your building to the architect to see whether it matches his or her idea.

Fig. 3.2. Task 9

Reflect 3.2

Figures 3.3, 3.4, and 3.5 show the work of prekindergartners, kindergartners, and first graders, respectively, on task 9.

- What do you assess about these students' understanding of 3-D compositions and decompositions?

- What questions would you ask or comments would you make to help you assess their understanding further?

Figure 3.3 shows the work of two pairs of prekindergartners on task 9. Paul and Matt were one architect-and-builder pair, and Elisa and Tucker were another. Paul's drawing of his structure (fig. 3.3b) indicates that he recognized the shapes of the blocks' faces—triangles in two sizes (and two colors—red and blue, shown here in gray scale) and squares (orange) at opposite ends of his structure. He added two more unusually shaped blocks (blue in his drawing), possibly showing several shapes composed together. Note that he was unaware of the relationships among the blocks and did not connect them in any way that showed those relationships. When Matt was given the drawing only, he was able to choose some blocks for the

a. Architect Paul's building

b. Architect Paul's plan for his building

(continued on pp. 80–81)

Fig. 3.3. Prekindergartners' responses to task 9: architects' plans (shown in photos and drawings) and builders' creations from the plans

c. Builder Matt's construction from Paul's plan in (b) and the photo in (a)

d. Architect Elisa's building (left) and her plan for it (right)

Fig. 3.3. *Continued*

building but was unable to create a structure. When he was shown the photograph, he said, "I can do this!" and quickly created the structure shown in figure 3.3c. It is worth noting that Matt selected the small "upside down" triangle first, couldn't get it to stand up, and then added the other larger triangular prisms. He also noted that his other small triangle wouldn't "stay up on the [larger] one," so he left it "down."

Figure 3.3d shows a photo of Elisa's structure (on the left) and her drawing (on the right). Her drawing represented the relationships between the blocks quite well, and the colors that she used for the block faces matched the colors of the blocks she had used. However, Elisa's drawing left out some blocks or did not include enough of

e. Builder Tucker's construction from Elisa's plan and the photo in (d)

Fig. 3.3. *Continued*

a particular block. When Tucker first looked at the drawing, he was able to begin building Elisa's structure, using the number of blocks that Elisa had pictured. Seeing that two blocks seemed to overlap in the drawing at the top of the structure, he asked for clarification: "Is that top one orange or red?" When he was shown the photograph of Elisa's building, he began correcting his structure immediately and then asked, "Should I make it like this [the photograph] or like this [the drawing]?" Tucker placed the blocks correctly; however, his orientation of the smaller triangular prisms and one of the larger ones was incorrect. When shown the photograph (in fig. 3.3) and asked whether his placement of the larger one was "right," he said, "It's backward," indicating his awareness of a difference in perspective from his own.

Figure 3.4 shows the work of kindergartners on the same task. In the first part of the task, when students act as architects, the kindergartners worked together in groups to create a block structure. Once they had completed their structure to their satisfaction, they drew it individually, with each student working from his or her own vantage point. Two architect groups then exchanged drawings and built what they saw, with group members working together without the aid of the photographs shown in the figure but with all the drawings from the different points of view. The results indicate that the student builders were able to create structures that were similar to those shown in the drawings, with some differences. The discussions in the builder groups included many orientation terms and descriptions of the solids, primarily using vocabulary related to two dimensions. When questioned about the task, one student referred to the drawings from multiple viewpoints: "Lots of drawings helped, but it's hard to draw them [the blocks] fat!"

a. Actual structure (above) and a sample drawing (below) from an architect

b. Builders' creation of the structure in (a) from drawings
from multiple vantage points

d. Builders' construction
of the structure pictured
in (c) from drawings from
all the architects in the
group, from multiple
vantage points

c. Sample drawing of a
different structure from
an architect

Fig. 3.4. Kindergartners' work in groups on task 9: sample drawings from
architects and builders' constructions from drawings

The photographs in figure 3.5 show first-grade architects' structures and drawings of them from different viewpoints. These first graders worked with partners to build a colorful structure with three-dimensional tangram blocks. The only

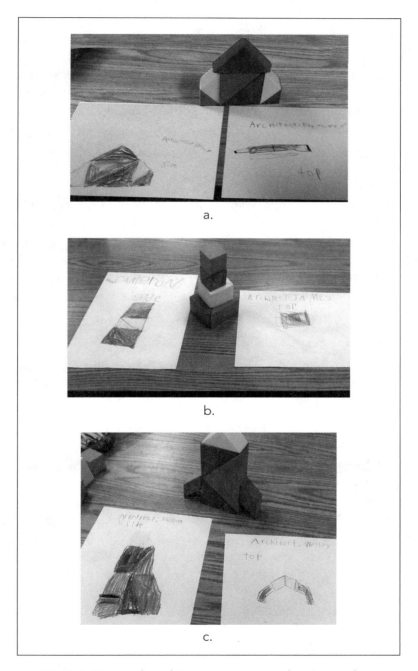

a.

b.

c.

Fig. 3.5. First-grade architects' structures and corresponding drawings from two vantage points: side and top-down

specification was that they use fewer than ten tangram blocks. Each partner drew the structure from either a side view or a top view. Generally, this task was difficult for these first graders—and one that they had never done before. The three drawings in figure 3.5 vary in detail and clarity of their labels. During the activity, one team of students asked to be allowed to tell everyone how to make a cube "look like a cube" instead of a square in the drawing. Everyone was quite impressed by these students' presentation and wanted to know whether a similar method might be used for drawing the "triangle one." How to draw a triangular prism with pencil and paper or technology, representing its three dimensions in a two-dimensional medium, was a question that held students' interest, and they continued to explore it during their free time.

Task 10: Building "frames" for 3–D shapes

Figure 3.6 presents task 10, which is appropriate for second graders. In this activity, students work with straws with pipe cleaners threaded through them to allow joining the straw "line segments" at the ends to form vertices. The students use these materials to create "frames" for three-dimensional shapes (prisms and pyramids) according to descriptions of the component two-dimensional shapes (triangles, rectangles, and pentagons). After examining task 10, consider the questions in Reflect 3.3.

Use straws threaded with pipe cleaners to create "frames" for 3-D shapes that are prisms and pyramids. Compose and name the 3-D shapes that have the following attributes:

a. This 3-D shape has only four triangular faces, and the faces are all the same size and shape.

b. This 3-D shape has six rectangular faces. Two of the faces are the same size and shape, and the other four faces are the same size and shape.

c. This 3-D shape has two triangular faces that are the same size and shape and three quadrilateral faces that are the same size and shape.

d. This 3-D shape has two faces that are pentagons of the same size and shape and five quadrilateral faces that are the same size and shape.

e. This 3-D shape has four triangular faces, all the same size and shape, and one square face.

Fig. 3.6. Task 10

Reflect 3.3

- How is task 10 (fig. 3.6) different from task 9 (fig. 3.2)?
- What could students learn about three-dimensional shapes and their composition from task 9 that would expand their thinking about the attributes of prisms and pyramids?

Task 10 encourages students to think about specific three-dimensional shapes—prisms and pyramids—as compositions of the two-dimensional shapes that form their faces. The second graders whose work is shown in figure 3.7 completed this task as a center activity. This is a difficult task for second graders, and these students' efforts to connect the two-dimensional shapes to form the three-dimensional shapes were a true demonstration of perseverance. Most students succeeded in making all the two-dimensional shapes specified in the descriptions and then tried to connect them. Making the connections to form the 3-D frames is the most challenging part of the task. When the students ended up with two line segments side by side rather than one line segment (along the edge of a solid, where the sides of two faces intersect), the teacher simply commented on the two line segments connecting the vertices and wondered aloud about how it could just be one line. The completed results shown in the figure illustrate frames made according to the listed criteria for shapes (a)–(e). One student commented that prisms were the "easiest because you could make two two-dimensional shapes and then connect them at all their points with one straw." Another student said "Pyramids are hard because you have lots of straws going together in just one point and the pipe cleaner gets lumpy."

Tasks 11 and 12: Decomposition and composition with 2-D shapes

Goldenberg and Clements (2014) state, "Children can learn to compose and decompose two-dimensional shapes in many . . . productive ways" (p. 78). Young students especially enjoy composing and decomposing two-dimensional shapes, and tasks 11 and 12 illustrate just two of the many possible activities that allow students to use these processes in a variety of ways. In fact, some of these ways can be used to measure the area of another two-dimensional shape.

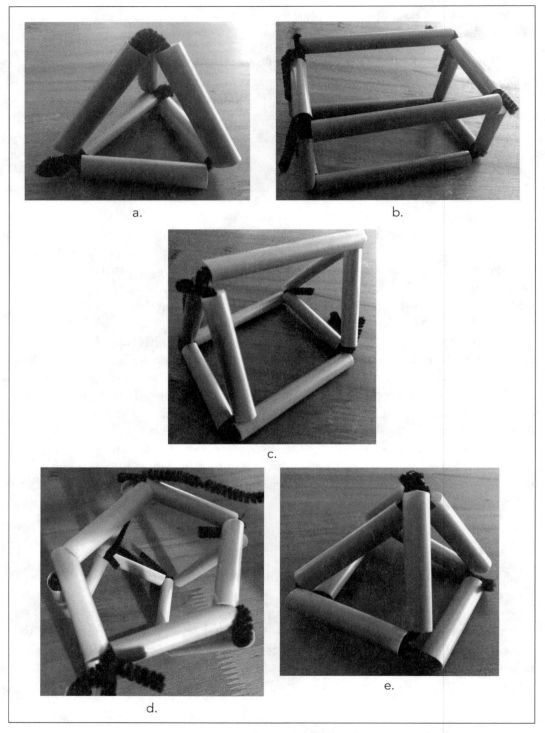

Fig. 3.7. Prisms and pyramids made by second graders
with straws threaded with pipe cleaners for task 10

Figure 3.8 presents task 11, in which students select two to five shapes from a set of triangles and rectangles made from 3-inch by 3-inch sticky notes and use them to compose other shapes. The task gives instructions for making the component shapes, which include triangles and rectangles, both in two sizes (and the smaller rectangles are squares). The students (first or second graders) place their new shapes on paper, outline them, place sticky dots to represent their vertices, and then name them, using a geometric term. Examine the task and then consider the questions in Reflect 3.4.

Choose two, three, four, or five shapes from the group of triangles and rectangles shown below, and use the shapes that you have selected to make new 2-D shapes. Arrange your new shapes on paper and draw an outline around them. Use sticky dots to mark their vertices, and name your new shapes.

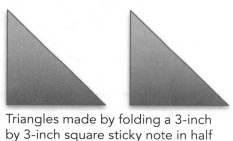 

Triangles made by folding a 3-inch by 3-inch square sticky note in half

Smaller triangles made by folding larger triangles in half and cutting them on the fold

Rectangles made by folding a 3-inch by 3-inch square sticky note in half

Smaller rectangles (squares) made by folding larger rectangles in half and cutting them on the fold

Fig. 3.8. Task 11

Reflect 3.4

- How could task 11 (fig. 3.8) increase students' knowledge of shapes and possible compositions?

- What questions could you ask, or comments could you make, about students' work on this task that would facilitate their later understanding of area measurement?

Obviously, this task presents students with many possibilities for composing new shapes. Figure 3.9 shows just a few of those that a group of first and second graders produced. The conversations that occurred as the students worked demonstrated their understanding of shapes and the many different ways in which they can be composed. As with other tasks in this book, these discussions were both insightful and informative about their understanding.

In fact, while the students worked and conversed, they made a number of important connections. For example, the student who made the quadrilateral shown in part (b) of figure 3.9 said, "I think it is a parallelogram, but I know for sure it is a quadrilateral! (I also don't know how to spell *parallelogram*.)" The student who made the hexagon in (e) said, "This hexagon doesn't look like the normal one," apparently thinking of the yellow hexagon pattern block. Two students noted that both the hexagon in (e) and the rectangle in (f) used two triangles and two squares but were different shapes. Then one student noted that the two triangles in the rectangle were the same size, but the two triangles in the hexagon were different sizes, and the teacher made an additional comment: "I wonder if you could take apart the same exact shapes that made the hexagon and make a different shape . . . Or perhaps you could do the same thing with the shapes that made the rectangle . . ." The students accepted the challenge and were surprised to be able to make a pentagon with the shapes composing the hexagon by moving just the small triangle—and to be able to make an octagon by moving just one of the small squares. They shared their discoveries with others in the class, and together the students found that "almost all shapes could be changed by moving just one shape!" Although the students found that all shapes could be changed, they wanted to add the word *almost* because they hadn't tried all shapes!

Task 12, shown in figure 3.10, is set in a quilt-making context and can help to build students' understanding of composing and decomposing, or *partitioning*, shapes. Making quilt squares is a common activity for students—and adults—of all ages. This task, in which students cover a six-inch by six-inch quilt square with isosceles right triangles whose equal sides are three inches, was used with second graders as they were beginning to talk about equal shares and partitioning shapes. Before beginning the task, students created a triangle by folding a three-inch by three-inch sticky note in half along a diagonal (with the sticky side folded inside). Using only their single triangle, they then predicted how many equal-sized triangles they would need to completely cover a six-inch by six-inch square of white paper. Consider the questions in Reflect 3.5 before examining the student work shown below.

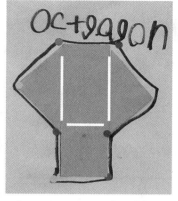

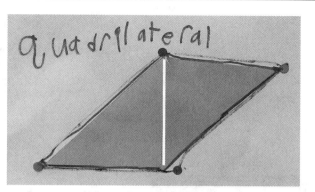

b. A quadrilateral made with two triangles

a. An octagon made with two
triangles and two rectangles,
one of which is a square

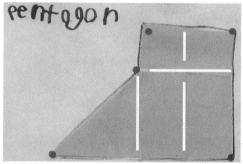

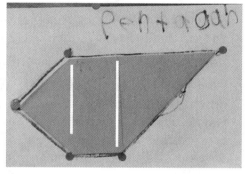

c. A pentagon made with four
rectangles and a triangle

d. A pentagon made with two triangles
(different sizes) and a rectangle

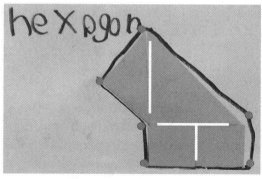

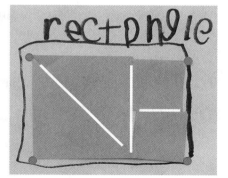

e. A hexagon made with two squares
and two triangles

f. A rectangle made with two
triangles and two squares

Fig. 3.9. Two-dimensional shapes composed by first and second graders
working with triangles and rectangles in task 11

Select equal-sized triangles in two different colors. Completely cover a six-inch by six-inch square of white paper with the colored triangles to make a quilt square. Do not overlap the triangles or leave gaps between the triangles. When you are finished, use fractions to label each triangle, considering the square of white paper as 1 whole. Write an equation to describe all the triangles in your quilt square.

Fig. 3.10. Task 12

Reflect 3.5

Task 12 (fig. 3.10) asks students how many isosceles right triangles with legs of three inches they will need to cover a six-inch by six-inch quilt square without gaps or overlaps.

- How would you expect students to solve this problem? What strategies do you think they would be likely to use to make their predictions?

- How could you use this task to lead to the measurement of area?

- What geometry or measurement vocabulary would you expect to hear from students as they worked on this task? What comments would help you assess students' understanding of decomposition or composition and prepare them to build on their understanding to develop ideas related to measurement?

A lively conversation developed in this group of very motivated second graders as they completed many quilt squares. Their remarks to one another included the following:

- "It [the triangle] doesn't fit just any way."

- "You need to make four squares [with the triangles] for it to work!" [When a partner questioned the statement, the student demonstrated by putting two triangles together to make a square and then modeling the fit of four squares in the six-inch by six-inch square.]

- "I think you will need eight triangles because $2 + 2 + 2 + 2$."

- "I thought you would need nine 'cause I think it is more than eight."

- "If I used four triangles of one color and four triangles of another color, half of it is one color, and half of it is another color."

- "Four of my triangles are one color, and four of my triangles are another color. That would be four of the eight are pink, and four of the eight are blue."

- "Just cut one triangle in half . . . and you get nine triangles!" [This comment was offered by a student who predicted that it would take nine triangles to completely cover the white square. The remark prompted a good discussion of why that wouldn't work. Students supported their reasoning by showing that the two half triangles would not make triangles that were the same size as the others.]

This activity was given to students near the end of the school year, after they had experiences with equations, unit fractions, and making equal shares from rectangles and circles. Students had little difficulty in drawing on this knowledge to write equations using unit fractions to represent their work on the quilt squares as shown in figure 3.11. However, their comments during the activity made it obvious that they had some misconceptions about fraction concepts. After their squares were completed and presented to their classmates, a lively discussion ensued, with students supporting or justifying their ideas.

The squares that the students produced for this task were quite interesting and varied, and the results provided many opportunities for interactions. Spatial terms, shape classifications, measurement concepts, and transformation of shapes and objects were all evident in these conversations about the students' two-dimensional creations.

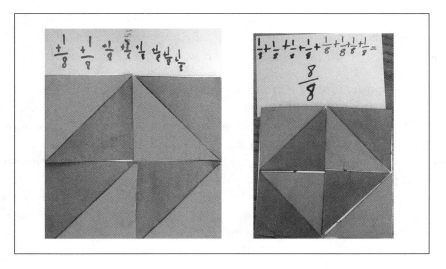

Fig. 3.11. Second graders' covering of six-inch by six-inch quilt squares with triangles in two colors and their equations to represent their work

Summarizing Pedagogical Content Knowledge to Support Essential Understanding 4*d*

Teaching the mathematical ideas in this chapter requires specialized knowledge related to the four components presented in the Introduction: learners, curriculum, instructional strategies, and assessment. The four sections that follow summarize some examples of these specialized knowledge bases in relation to Essential Understanding 4*d*. Although we separate them to highlight their importance, we also recognize that they are connected and support one another.

Knowledge of learners

Many have observed that if children are enjoying an activity, they do not know when they are playing and when they are learning. This observation certainly describes students' engagement with the activities in this chapter. As mentioned by Goldenberg and Clements (2014, p. 78), teachers often think of block building as play and therefore distinct from mathematics learning when in reality children are *both* playing *and* learning!

Although many comments could be made about the learners and learning discussed in this chapter, two observations are particularly useful. First, the four activities presented in tasks 9–12 were clearly very enjoyable for students, and their enjoyment promoted productive engagement, persistence, and problem solving. Students derived pleasure and satisfaction from experimenting with both two- and three-dimensional shapes; in fact, they spent much of their usual classroom free time working on quilt pieces, making drawings of shape constructions, or creating shapes from straws or paper shapes. And, most important, they interacted verbally with their peers as they worked on the tasks, helping one another, clarifying their understanding, and justifying their solutions or creations.

Second, the responses to the tasks made it obvious that these students needed more experiences with these types of activities. Maturation differences were evident in students' work (especially on those tasks requiring fine motor skills). However, the differences were primarily in experience levels. Some students had worked often with blocks; others had little or no block-building experience. Some students seemingly had a sense of how shapes looked and would fit together; others appeared never to have done a puzzle or pieced together shapes to fill a space. For the most part, this chapter includes only "good" results. There certainly were other results that showed that some students initially had little or no understanding of what they were to do. However, with their peers' tutoring, more experiences, and encouragement from their teachers, they were able to complete the tasks in a manner that gave them satisfaction and moved them forward in understanding.

Knowledge of curriculum

As shown in the list at the beginning of this chapter, the Common Core State Standards for Mathematics address the composition and decomposition of two- and three-dimensional shapes at all three grade levels, K–2. Unfortunately, the concepts of composition and decomposition are difficult to teach with a typical mathematics textbook, which does not include manipulatives or technology that allows students to experiment with composing or decomposing shapes. In addition, teachers often do not have the materials that students need to compose and decompose shapes. This is especially true for three-dimensional shapes, some of which are thought of as prekindergarten or kindergarten "toys"—not as appropriate tools for first and second graders.

Working through composing and decomposing tasks with materials like three-dimensional tangram blocks, straws, and sticky notes develops young students' understanding and builds a strong foundation for later learning. However, many teachers believe that they must focus on number and the curriculum that will be tested. They often think that they do not have time to introduce these types of materials and hands-on activities, which they often regard simply as "fun," sometimes remarking, "Block building isn't on our test!" The activities in this chapter and others like them provide students with experiences that give them the understanding called for in the Common Core State Standards. Stated simply, the curriculum needs to be expanded to include investigations of the decomposition and composition of both two- and three-dimensional shapes.

Knowledge of instructional strategies

Teachers can draw on a wide range of instructional strategies to help their students understand composing and decomposing two- and three-dimensional shapes. As in teaching the concepts in the previous chapters, three specific strategies are critical and should be emphasized: (1) making "I wonder" comments to motivate and challenge students and listening attentively to their responses, (2) integrating other mathematics content into geometric content related to composition and decomposition, and (3) differentiating instruction to match objectives and student needs.

Throughout most of the activities discussed in this chapter, students responded positively to their teachers' "I wonder" comments. Because engaged, effective teachers find themselves saying "I wonder . . ." a great deal in the classroom, those statements are not usually hard to make. What is hard, however, is remaining quiet and letting students respond to their peers or watching them as they act out a solution to an "I wonder" statement. The best part of this strategy is that students start making their own "I wonder" statements. In fact, in one first-grade classroom, the teacher began writing "I wonder" statements—her students' as well as her own—and together she and her students became a class that had fun making many geometric discoveries!

Integrating students' experiences with composition and decomposition of shapes with other mathematics content is important to their learning. Having students write an equation containing unit fractions to describe the triangles composing their quilt squares makes a natural connection with fraction concepts. In another, related activity, a group of second graders covered the same square by placing four blue triangles on one side and four pink triangles on the other side. When asked what they saw, they responded that ½ of the area of the square was pink and ½ of it was blue. They were then asked to decompose the square and compose the tri-angles in a square again in any arrangement that they chose. Next, they discussed whether the square was still ½ blue and ½ pink. After some interesting discussion, the students decided that indeed each square was ½ blue and ½ pink. The students then put their squares together to form a large quilt (see fig. 3.12, in which pink and blue show as different shades of gray), counted the total number of blue tri-angles and the total number of pink triangles, and "discovered" that the whole quilt was half pink and half blue.

The third instructional strategy involves focusing on students' needs and differ-entiating instruction to help students meet different expectations. For example, activities, and goals for activities, can vary according to the grade level. Essentially

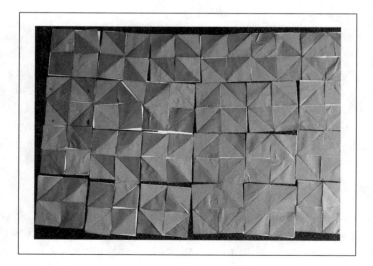

Fig. 3.12. "Quilt" made from second-grade students' individual quilt squares composed of triangles, half of them pink and half of them blue (in gray scale)

the same quilt-making activity can benefit students in K–grade 2 in different ways, eliciting different insights and supporting different concepts. Kindergartners can fold squares into rectangles and make some beautiful quilt squares that can be assembled into a paper quilt. Kindergartners often consider making a quilt to be an enjoyable puzzle, and their teachers often regard it as an activity that addresses the learning objective of composing two-dimensional shapes. First graders can follow the same initial process but use triangles rather than rectangles and work with a choice of three different colors. Like the kindergartners, they will be proud of their creations, which will give them an opportunity to see the beauty and patterns of geometry! Once they have assembled the larger quilt, they can begin to identify many different shapes embedded in it. They can list their discoveries or count all the different shape compositions. Figure 3.13 shows a quilt made by first graders, whose discoveries included the following:

- The large pink shape [dark gray in fig. 3.13] on the bottom [located slightly left of center] is an octagon.

- Four triangles put together with their long sides out make a square that looks like a diamond.

- Six triangles put together can make a hexagon. [See medium gray L shape on bottom left.]

- Two triangles with matched short sides can make a bigger triangle.

Second graders can integrate other mathematical ideas and processes into their work with quilt squares, as discussed earlier and demonstrated in figure 3.11.

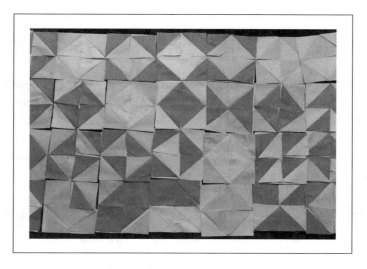

Fig. 3.13. A three-color "quilt" made by first graders

Knowledge of assessment

Observing is the primary method for assessment of students' development of Essential Understanding 4d. Listening to what students say and watching what they do reveal a great deal about the conjectures they are making on the basis of data they have collected and by applying their critical thinking skills. As the information presented after each sample of student work demonstrates, specific information can be assessed by paying close attention to students' responses and by carefully inspecting their creations. Those specific assessments are important, especially for individual students.

Further, students' perseverance can often be assessed from their work on these activities. When students in one class were making the straw-and-pipe-cleaner constructions, two students worked on all the ways to make triangles using straws of different lengths. They persisted in their work on this problem for a week, using center time or recess to create a large sample of shapes. They reported that "some triangles just can't be made!" They demonstrated this by showing three straight line segments with lengths of four inches, three inches, and one inch. They had just discovered a geometric theorem!

Research often reports on the short attention spans of young children. In most cases, students did not demonstrate short attention spans on these tasks. They composed and decomposed, and decomposed and composed, until they got the shapes that they wanted. They also seemed willing to encourage their peers to work on the problem as well. Most students spent more than an hour on most of the tasks with little teacher intervention.

Conclusion

This chapter has focused on decomposing and composing two- and three-dimensional shapes. As the activities and samples of student work have illustrated, decomposition and composition, the focus of Essential Understanding 4d, are interconnected with essential understandings related to all the geometry and measurement concepts. The next chapter emphasizes measurement of geometric shapes and the essential understandings that directly connect geometry with measurement, and the process of exploring these will involve visiting some of the activities in this chapter again.

practice

Chapter 4
Measuring Geometric Attributes

Big Idea 4
One way to analyze and describe geometric objects, relationships among them, or the spaces that they occupy is to quantify—measure or count—one or more of their attributes.

Essential Understanding 4a
Measurement can specify "how much" by assigning a number to such attributes as length, area, volume, and angle.

Essential Understanding 4b
Some quantities can be compared or measured directly, others can be measured indirectly, and the measurements of some objects are computed from other measurements.

Essential Understanding 4c
Measurement can be performed with a variety of units. The size of the unit and the number of units in the measure are inversely related to each other.

Essential Understanding 4d
Objects can be decomposed and composed to facilitate their measurement.

Measuring requires a "complex combination of concepts and skills" (Clements and Sarama 2009, p. 167) and is one of the most important real-world applications of mathematics. Learning the process of measuring and developing skill in measurement take years, and the concepts that students learn in pre-K–grade 2 are foundational to their later understanding. This chapter focuses primarily on the essential understandings associated with and supporting Big Idea 4 and the relationship of these concepts to the geometric attributes of shape (Chapter 1), the location or orientation of shapes in space (Chapter 2), and the decomposition and composition of shapes so that they can be measured (Chapter 3).

Working toward Big Idea 4 through Essential Understandings 4*a*–4*d*

Understanding the idea of measurement and the process of measuring requires grasping a number of foundational concepts, including ideas of transitivity, iteration and equal partitioning, conservation, and origin. These ideas can be summed up briefly as follows:

- **Transitivity:** If $A > B$ and $B > C$, then $A > C$. Or if $A < B$ and $B < C$, then $A < C$. Or if $A = B$ and $B = C$, then $A = C$.

- **Iteration and equal partitioning:** Two fundamental processes in measurement are subdividing length or area into equal units (partitioning) and then repeating the unit by placing equal-sized units end-to-end or side-by-side (iterating) and counting them to obtain a measurement consisting of a number of units.

- **Conservation:** In measurement, conservation is the principle that an object "maintains the same size and shape if it is rearranged, transformed, or divided in various ways" (Chapin and Johnson 2006, p. 272). For example, if two objects have the same length, their lengths remain the same and equal, regardless of their individual orientations. If two squares that have the same area are partitioned differently (one into two congruent triangles and the other into two congruent rectangles, for instance), the squares still have the same areas. In other words, their measurements are conserved, regardless of their arrangement, transformation, or partitions.

- **Origin:** The origin is the point where a measurement begins. For a correct measurement, the origin must be known, and measurements must begin at the same point to be compared.

Young students begin to develop rudiments of these fundamental concepts at a very early age. The following conversation overheard between two kindergartners at recess illustrates emerging ideas of transitivity:

Asa:	I am taller than Eli, and he is in first grade.
Joey:	Well, I am taller than you [*directly modeling his height by backing up to Asa*], so I am taller than Eli, too!
Asa:	I don't know . . . Let's see when we go inside.

Likewise, a group of young students who determined how far a cup airplane traveled on various flights by marking the distances with equal cash register tape lengths (see fig. 4.1a), were developing ideas related to iteration and equal partitioning. The tape represented length as a continuous quantity, and, after rolling it out on the floor to show the length of each flight, the students used rulers, placing them end-to-end (iterating), and counting the number of rulers to determine how many "rulers long" each flight was. Ideas about conservation may also begin to develop before kindergarten, as is evident in the following exchange between preschoolers asked to measure their arms:

Mandy: You can't measure your arm that way! [*pointing to the child's arm lying on the table*] Teacher showed us an arm standing like this [*showing her arm bent at the elbow with the upper arm perpendicular to the table*].

Beth: It's the same both ways! And it's easy to measure when it's flat!

Very young students have some rudimentary ideas about the significance of measuring from the same point, or origin, as well. Consider the drawing by four-year-old Anthony, shown in figure 4.1b, designed to show that he was "bigger" than his teacher. His height measurement certainly had a different origin from hers! Many of the student samples presented in this chapter reflect children's development of these concepts.

Precise language for talking about measurement is also a focus of this chapter. Young students love to compare the sizes of objects or people, often using very general terms, like *big*, *little*, or even *GI-MONGUS!* Statements like "My dad is bigger than your dad" (when talking about either strength or height), "Mary's ice cream is more bigger than mine," or "My sister is more little than me 'cause she's just a baby" are all measurement observations and represent very young students' efforts to offer descriptions of size and make comparisons, although the language that they use is mathematically imprecise. As students begin to focus on and identify the attributes that can be measured, they begin to realize that general descriptions of "bigger" or "smaller" are less useful than descriptions that are more precise and use words like *taller*, *tallest*, *longer*, *longest*, *shorter*, *shortest*, *heavier*, *heaviest*, *lighter*, and *lightest*, and phrases like "holds more," "holds less," "covers more," "covers less," "covers most," and "covers least."

Chapter 4 presents and discusses four tasks, numbered as tasks 13–16 in the sequence of tasks in the book. All but one of these tasks intentionally include the phrase "tools of your choice." Young students should see a variety of both standard and nonstandard tools used by adults and their peers as they begin to understand the process of measurement. These tools should consist of the following: rulers,

a.

b.

Fig. 4.1. Early work with measurement concepts: (a) using cash register tape
to mark the lengths of the flights of a cup airplane and
(b) "reimagining" heights by using different origins

yardsticks, metersticks, cash register tape strips, tape measures, pipe cleaners, inch-long pieces of straws connected by string or yarn, one-inch cubes, centimeter cubes, graduated cylinders in a variety of sizes, empty containers of various sizes, grid paper with different-sized units, and counters or ways to count using tools with equal and unequal lengths.

Task 13: Using different attributes in measurement comparisons

Figure 4.2 shows task 13, a comparison task with six subtasks, (a)–(f), each of which is focused on a different measurement attribute. Review this task and respond to the questions in Reflect 4.1. As you address the questions, consider several different grade levels and think about the vocabulary that you would expect students to use; the tools that you would expect them to choose, if any; and the processes that you would expect them to employ.

Compare, using tools of your choice:

a. The sizes of five different pieces of fruit. Which one is the biggest? Which one is the smallest?

b. The heights of five block towers. Which tower is the tallest? Which tower is the shortest?

c. The capacities of four different-sized containers. Which container holds the most water? Which container holds the least water?

d. The volumes of two different boxes. Which box holds more cubes? Which box holds fewer cubes?

e. The areas of five 2-D shapes. Which shape covers the most space? Which shape covers the least space?

f. Angles that are right angles and angles that are not right angles. What angles can you find that have "special square corners"? What angles do not have "special square corners"?

Fig. 4.2. Task 13

Reflect 4.1

- **When do young students make measurement comparisons in everyday life?**

- **What specific geometric attributes are students expected to compare in each part of task 13?**

- **What essential understanding or understandings does this task address?**

Young students naturally apply measurement comparisons in a variety of settings in school and other areas of everyday life. Hearing complaints on a basketball court concerning the fairness of a shooting game, one teacher gave students chalk and a meterstick to label the start line for each basketball shot. Students in another class who were launching balloon rockets were encouraged to identify the rocket that went the highest, using trees on the playground for height comparisons. In a different group, students were preparing presents for a family event at their school and had to compare the sizes of three pieces of wrapping paper and select the one that would completely cover the gift. Still other students were sharing treats with their peers and had to compare the sizes of the treats so that everyone received a fair share—and then the students had to explain how they had made their determinations. These common examples illustrate just a few of the opportunities that, if used to advantage, can help students develop an understanding of measurement.

Each part of task 13 addresses comparison with a different attribute, and each subtask provides students with an opportunity to use different tools, vocabulary, and measuring processes. Essential Understanding 4b—"Some quantities can be compared or measured directly, [and] others can be measured indirectly"—is the primary concept addressed by this task, but Essential Understanding 4a also comes into play, with its focus on assigning numbers to "such attributes as length, area, volume, and angle." Each of the subtasks was set up as an activity in a measuring center in a multi-age (pre-K–grade 2) classroom.

Subtask 13a: Finding an attribute for comparing pieces of fruit

Subtask 13a is an open-ended comparison task that requires students to think about a variety of ways to compare five pieces of fruit and decide which is "biggest" and which is "smallest." The terms *biggest* and *smallest* were used intentionally to see how students would interpret the attribute to compare to make the determination. Students' responses varied. The photograph in figure 4.3a shows how one group of students arranged a banana, a mango, an apple, a nectarine, and a plum from "smallest" to "biggest." As a second grader, Trace, explained, "You use a ruler" to tell the "biggest length." When asked to show what he meant, Trace measured the length of the banana and the other pieces of fruit by placing the ruler on top of each and ignoring the circumference. Some students used pipe cleaners, one of which appears in figure 4.3a, to "go around" pieces of fruit, but they did not appear to use these tools when they compared the fruits. When asked why they did not put pipe cleaners around the banana, they said that it was "long."

Parts (b), (c), and (d) of figure 4.3 show how other children in the same classroom measured pieces of fruit to determine which was "biggest" or "smallest." Figure 4.3b

Fig. 4.3. Responses from students in a
multi-age classroom (pre-K–grade 2) to subtask 13a

shows the efforts of a kindergartner, Jorge, to measure the length of the banana. He used a ruler and then asked Trace what numbers he should use. Trace explained that he had to start with "the zero" at one end and "use the words *inches* and *centimeters*." Figure 4.3c shows Trace's demonstration of how to measure the "length" of a nectarine, and figure 4.3d shows the idea of another student, Ford, to use another attribute, weight. Ford demonstrated by hefting pieces of fruit in his hands and said, "The mango is heavier than the banana, so it is the biggest!"

Subtask 13b: Comparing lengths

Subtask 13b is a length comparison task in which students are asked to assess the relative heights of five block towers. This task highlights the specific attribute of height by using the words *taller* and *shorter*. In the multi-age classroom, two of the five towers were placed next to each other, and the other three were dispersed around the room intentionally so that students could not use direct comparison (see fig. 4.4). One was on top of a bookcase, another was on a table, and another was on the floor. In fact, in an effort to be helpful, one student told the teacher, "If you put all the towers right next to each other, it would be better and easier to do!"

In the case of the two side-by-side towers, students said that the tower on the right was "taller" than the tower on the left (see fig. 4.4a). However, when asked how they knew, they responded, "Because it looks like it." One student said that the window blinds behind the towers helped him, "'cause [the tower on the right] went up more." Further, the tower on the right was composed of just three blocks, whereas the tower on the left was composed of six blocks. When students were asked why the tower with *more* blocks was shorter than the tower with *fewer* blocks, their responses reflected their mastery of vocabulary. One preschooler made a vertical motion with his index finger and said, "'Cause the blocks over there go up, and"–changing to a horizontal motion with his finger—"those go down." A first grader said, "It just makes a difference how you put the block . . . number doesn't matter!"

Students attempted to use rulers to measure the height of each of the other three towers placed around the room. Some students measured incorrectly, and others measured correctly. Most ignored the numbers on the ruler and just measured from the bottom of the ruler to where the ruler hit the top of the tower. Unfortunately, that procedure proved to be impossible in the case of the tower on top of the bookcase, so some students simply said it was the "tallest," even though it was not. Some older students used the numbers on the ruler and labeled the numbers as *inches, centimeters,* or, in some cases, both. The students who measured correctly succeeded in identifying the tallest and shortest towers; however, they measured each tower individually and gave no evidence of an understanding of transitivity.

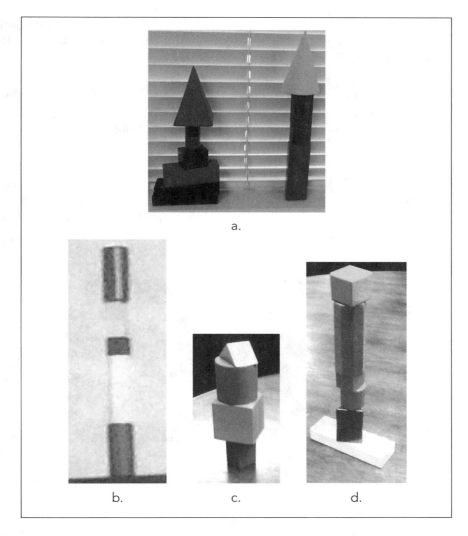

Fig. 4.4. Five towers, arranged so that (a) two are side by side, and (b–d) three were separated from one another in different locations around the room

Subtask 13c: Comparing capacities

Comparisons of capacity, rather than of volume, are the focus of subtask 13c, in which students compare four different-sized containers with respect to this attribute. The *volume* (the term used in Essential Understanding 4*a*) of a three-dimensional object is the amount of space that the object occupies. Typically, measuring the volume of an object involves finding the number of cubes, or cubic units, that would fit inside it or fill it. In subtask 13d, students make a comparison of two boxes that involves measurements of the type commonly used to compare objects with respect to the geometric attribute of volume. Because volume is often a large number, even in the case of small containers, and because cubes often do not fit well in commonly found containers, subtask 13c asks students to compare capacities of containers that are commonly found at a water or sand table. Capacity is used for the measure of liquids or to describe the size of containers that hold liquids. Note that this comparison task uses the phrases "holds the most" and "holds the least" to highlight the specific attribute of capacity.

Figure 4.5 shows four containers used in subtask 13c in the multi-age classroom. An interesting dialogue developed among four students and the teacher during work on this task. (All four students were at different grade levels: Susie was a prekindergartner; David, a kindergartner; Debbie, a first grader; and John, a second grader.)

Fig. 4.5. Four containers for comparison with respect to capacity

Teacher:	[*Showing a pitcher of water colored green with food coloring*] Which container will hold the largest amount of green water?
Susie:	The big one [*pointing to the tall flared vase*] . . . 'Cause it's big!
David:	Yeah, but it's skinny right here [*pointing to the middle of the vase*] . . . I think this one [*pointing to the jar with a handle*] because it's fat . . . No . . . Just a minute . . . [*Picks up the cup shown on the far left in the figure and looks at the opening.*] This one is fat too, but it's got a cup inside, so I still think it's this one [*pointing again to the jar with a handle*].

[*Other students seem to agree with David.*]

| Debbie: | Let's just fill them up and see. |

[*Without commenting, the teacher fills each of the containers with green water. The students watch and then look at the teacher expectantly.*]

Teacher: So how does this help us know which one holds the most?

John: We could measure the water . . . Like see how many spoonfuls of water there are and count them . . .

David: That's a lot of counting!

John: We could use bigger spoons, or maybe cups, to count.

[*The discussion continues and is mainly focused on who can count the highest. No one besides John seems to believe that getting bigger spoons or cups would help to lower the count.*]

Teacher: What if we empty all the green water in each container *except* the one we think will hold the most water? If we think that this container [*indicating the jar with a handle*] holds the most green water, and we pour all that water into this empty container [*holding up the container on the far right—the one that most students think holds the least*], what would happen?

David: It would spill out everywhere!

Susie: It would be a mess!

Teacher: Let's try it!

[*The teacher empties all the containers except the one with the handle and then pours all the water into the emptied container on the right, spilling some out. The students excitedly celebrate their prediction.*]

Teacher: So what do we know about the containers?

[*The students respond with a variety of ideas, from correct generalizations such as that the jar with a handle holds more water than the container on the far right to overgeneralizations such as that the jar with a handle holds the most water—more than any of the others.*]

Teacher: Let's put these plastic containers in the water table center, and you can try out your predictions there. We will talk about this next week in our group time! Good thinking, everyone!

Subtask 13d: Comparing volumes

Subtask 13d changes the focus from capacity to volume. First and second graders in the multi-age classroom worked on this subtask in two parts. First, they compared the sizes of three empty boxes by using tools of their choice. Figure 4.6a shows the work of a first grader, Tyler, and figure 4.6b shows the work of a second grader, Simon, as they tried to fill two different boxes. Tyler filled his box with centimeter cubes and attempted to count them many times, each time losing count. He decided not to finish the count because the blocks were just "too many to count today!" Simon filled the bottom of his box with six one-inch cubes and then said, "There are two layers, so I know twelve cubes will fit in this box." When he noticed Tyler's counting difficulty, he suggested that Tyler also use the larger cubes because then he wouldn't need so many. Figure 4.6c shows the work of a prekindergartner, Jorge, who joined the group and filled a box with different-sized cubes, in the process demonstrating that he did not yet understand the need for same-sized units in a measurement.

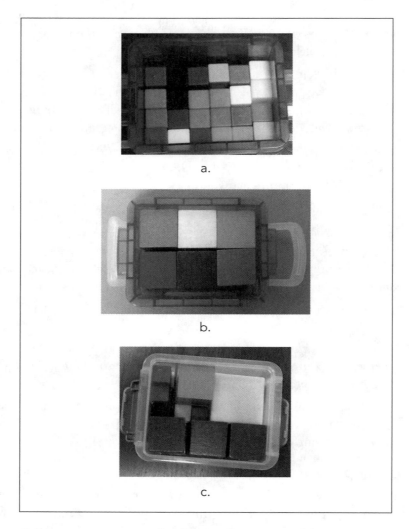

a.

b.

c.

Fig. 4.6. Responses to subtask 13d by (a) Tyler, a first grader,
(b) Simon, a second grader, and (c) Jorge, a prekindergartner

In the second part of the task, the students were shown two wrapped "mystery" boxes and asked to compare the volumes and find the number of centimeter cubes that would fill them completely. For this task, "boxes" had been constructed in advance from base-ten blocks that were taped together and then covered completely with wrapping paper. The students were encouraged to use other base ten-blocks or centimeter cubes to create boxes that were the same sizes as the mystery boxes to compare the volumes of the two boxes. As the students compared the boxes with respect to the attribute of volume, they used similar comparison terms as in task 13c: "contains more" and "contains less."

Subtask 13e: Comparing areas

In subtask 13e, students compare the areas of five two-dimensional shapes. This comparison task highlights the specific attribute to be compared by the phrases "covers the most space" and "covers the least space." In the multi-age classroom, the teacher gave students the five different tangram pieces shown and numbered in figure 4.7a, with one piece that they could identify easily as "covering the most space" and one that they could identify just as easily as "covering the least space." The other three pieces, although different in shape, were actually identical in area. Figure 4.7b shows the students' eventual arrangement of the tangram pieces from the one "taking least space" to the one "taking most space," with the three shapes identified as taking equal space displayed in a column in the middle.

As soon as these students saw the shapes, they identified shape 1 as the one that covered the most space and shape 4 as the one that covered the least space. When asked how they knew that these shapes were identified correctly, several students said simply, "Because they look like it." When the teacher indicated that she was not convinced by that statement, one student placed shape 1 on top of all the other shapes to demonstrate that it was "bigger" because nothing "stuck out." Another student selected grid paper and tried to count the squares under a tracing of the shape, but he got confused when he counted and was not sure what to do with the partial squares that were covered.

A similar discussion occurred when the students explained why shape 4 covered the least space. This time however, something very interesting occurred. When a student placed shape 4—the smallest triangle—on top of shapes 2, 3, and 5, another student noticed that the shape 4 triangle covered exactly half of shape 2 (the square) and that two of the shape 4 triangles would cover shape 2 completely. Several students continued to decompose shapes 3 and 5—the parallelogram and the middle-sized triangle, respectively—by placing triangles the size of shape 4 on top of them. One of the older students ultimately concluded that shapes 2, 3, and 5 "cover the same space!" Not everyone was convinced, and some continued to reason, "They are not the same . . . They don't look like it!"

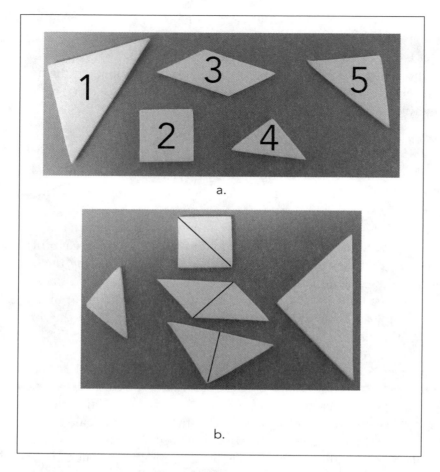

Fig. 4.7. Students worked on subtask 13e with (a) five tangram pieces, which they (b) arranged in order from "covering the least space" to "covering the most space," with the three shapes discovered to cover equal space in the middle.

Subtask 13f: Comparing by identifying right angles

Identifying right angles and angles that are not 90 degrees is the focus of the comparison in subtask 13f. This is an important activity, especially because "four right angles" is a defining attribute of a rectangle, and students need to have an understanding of what a right angle is and what it is not. Note, however, that the term *right angle* does not need to be used with young students. Because students have other meanings for *right* and may think that the opposite of a "right angle" is a "wrong angle" or even a "left angle," the name "square corner," or "special square corner," may be used instead, along with a square-corner detector to find these special angles.

Figure 4.8 illustrates the use of a square-corner detector made from a transparent sheet of plastic. To detect a right angle, the students match one vertex of the detector with the vertex of the corner that they are testing. Then they check to see whether the rays forming that corner's sides line up (in position but not in length) with the segments forming the sides of the square corner on the detector. If they do, the angle is a square corner or a right angle. In the multi-age classroom, students placed penguin counters on the special square corners that they found, including those formed by square tiles on the floor, horizontal shelves and vertical supports on a bookcase, and the corners of square work mats on desks. In less than thirty minutes, they had identified more than one hundred square corners in the classroom. They had a harder time finding angles that were *not* square corners, but they finally identified angles on a trapezoidal tabletop and the hinge of the art easel as not special square corners.

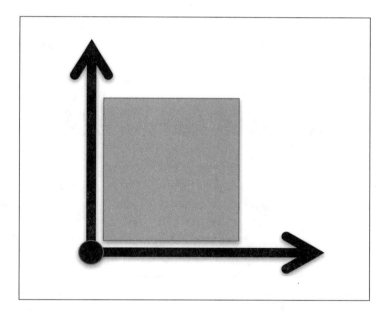

Fig. 4.8. Use of a square-corner detector

Assessing understanding from students' responses to subtasks 13a–13f

It is useful to reconsider the responses to subtasks (a)–(f) in task 13 and reflect on the understanding that students demonstrate and develop as they work with different geometric attributes to make comparisons. Use the questions in Reflect 4.2 to guide your review of students' work on the six subtasks in task 13.

Reflect 4.2

- Look back at the responses of students to subtasks 13a–13f discussed above and shown in figures 4.3–4.8. What do these students appear to have understood or misunderstood in each of the comparing tasks?

- What activities do you think could help students who respond as these students did and support continued growth of their abilities to compare geometric attributes?

The students who responded to subtask 13a could not clearly define the attribute that they were using to compare the five pieces of fruit. In general, they gravitated to length, although they appear to have given brief consideration to circumference and weight. Circumference would have been another way to determine "biggest" and "smallest." Experiences with three-dimensional objects and various tools (for example, measuring tapes, pipe cleaners, straws cut into one-inch pieces threaded with strings, etc.) could have helped them "measure around" the objects. Experiences with weight scales would have given them another tool for use in making comparisons, allowing them to measure the heaviness of objects in a more precise way than by holding the pieces of fruit in their hands. Further, Trace's explanation of how to use a ruler (see fig. 4.3c) indicated only a partial understanding of length measurement. He knew that unit labels would be centimeters or inches, and he had an idea of beginning at an origin (and suggested starting at zero), but he apparently did not yet understand that he could start anywhere on the ruler and count the number of units covered by the length of the object (or calculate by finding the difference between the beginning and ending points).

The students' efforts to compare the heights of the five towers in subtask 13b suggest that these students were familiar with this type of task and had used rulers to measure heights or lengths before. Because four of the five towers were shorter than twelve inches, a ruler was an excellent tool for the students to use. Their measuring of the heights of the towers by using the ruler for comparison only (simply seeing where it "hit" the top of a tower without referring to numbers on it) indicated that these students knew that they should work with the same point of origin for all five towers and that the "hit" would give them the information that they needed for the length. However, this method proved difficult because they could not always remember where the ruler hit, nor could they compare more than two towers at a time without using numbers. The concept of transitivity would have been particularly useful in this task. In the case of the side-by-side towers, the students easily determined which one was taller, and they could have used that information to help them find the tallest or shortest tower by reasoning, "Tower A is taller than tower B. But I know that tower C is taller than tower A, so it is also taller than tower B, and I don't need to measure B!"

Most students who worked on subtask 13c needed to see a comparison between two containers before comparing all four containers. Even if water tables are not available in classrooms, students should experiment with water to compare capacities of a variety of containers. Plastic tubs with plastic sheeting for spillage should be common tools in early childhood classrooms to help students learn to compare capacities. After experimenting with the different containers, students compared the tall flared vase with the short container that appears on the far right in figure 4.5. Most students correctly predicted that the short container would hold more water than the tall vase. (See Dougherty et al. [2010, p. 12] for a useful discussion of young students' thinking related to this comparison.)

As discussed, the students who completed subtask 13d compared the volumes of boxes in two different ways. First, they considered three empty boxes, and then they analyzed two mystery boxes that were already filled with cubes. Filling boxes with cubes can reveal developmental differences in students' understanding. Younger students often concentrate only on filling the box without attending to cube size or gaps between cubes. Tyler, the first grader whose work is described, focused on using equal-sized cubes, but when counting by ones, he could not get a correct count. The second grader, Simon, exhibited an understanding of measurement concepts when he used one-inch cubes to make one layer and did not need to fill the box completely to find the total number of cubes. The mystery box activity demonstrated that students could count by hundreds and tens and could understand that volume included three attributes—namely, height, length, and width. These students would require many more experiences to develop their understanding further (all students in the group reported that they had never done this before), along with explicit instruction about the measurement of the volume of small containers.

The students who compared the areas of five tangram shapes in response to subtask 13e appeared to find it easy to identify the shape that covered the most space and the shape that covered the least space. Both of these shapes were isosceles right triangles, though different in size, and the students were able to identify "biggest" and "smallest" just by sight: "They looked like it!" Stating additional reasons for their responses was more difficult. When the students placed the shapes on grids, they had a hard time counting the squares covered, but decomposing turned out to be an be easier and more productive strategy for analyzing and comparing all the shapes. Many students had difficulty believing that shapes 2, 3, and 5 covered the same space, even when two triangles like shape 4 were placed on top of each shape. These students might have benefited from additional hands-on opportunities to compose two congruent isosceles right triangles to make new shapes that look like shapes 2, 3, and 5. Or they might have been given paper tangrams and asked to decompose them by cutting or folding them into two right triangles.

Comparing angles by size was not the objective of subtask 13f; instead, the goal was to compare angles that were "special square corners" with angles that were not. All the students who responded to subtask 13f found and labeled square corners easily. Finding angles that were *not* square corners proved to be more difficult for these students, but most of them were able to recognize a few of the more obvious examples in their classroom. Although it seems likely that more practice would have been helpful, most of the students understood this comparison. To facilitate a more complete understanding of angle size, teachers might give their students straw angle makers (a flexible straw with a more rigid straw inserted in it) and encourage them to create a right angle, angles smaller than a right angle, and angles larger than a right angle.

Task 14: Measuring length

Task 14, shown in figure 4.9, asks students to measure the length of their forearm and make a drawing of how they made the measurement so that their process can be shared with others. Review this task and the questions in Reflect 4.3, and consider how students with different experiences might complete the task.

Measure the length of your forearm (from your elbow to the tip of your tallest finger), using measuring tools of your choice. How long is your forearm? Make a drawing showing how you did the task so that your work can be shared with others.

Fig. 4.9. Task 14

Reflect 4.3

- How would you expect students with different measuring experiences to measure a specific length? What vocabulary, tools and processes do you think they would employ?

- What essential understandings would students' work on this task help them to develop?

Typically, prekindergartners have limited experience, if any, of measuring length or assigning a number to tell "how many" of any particular unit a certain length is. To explore their understanding, one teacher gave her prekindergartners a particular measuring tool—colored, soft plastic "worms" in one-inch, two-inch, three-inch, and four-inch lengths—and very specific directions. To show students exactly what they were to measure, the teacher rested her elbow on a table and held her forearm up vertically. She then said she wanted them to measure "the length of your arm from the elbow to the tip of your tallest finger," indicating that length with her other hand.

One student, Mark, asked the teacher to place all his worms "side to side" on his forearm (see fig 4.10a); he said that when he tried it, they fell off. Another student, Francisco, used worms of different sizes and measured the perimeter of his forearm rather than its length (see fig. 4.10b). A third student, Amy, covered the area of her forearm with worms of different sizes (see fig. 4.10c). When she found that she needed more worms than she had, she asked her classmates to share so that she could "fill all the spaces." A fourth student, Kristen, recorded only her handprint and then used worms to mark out the fingers (see fig. 4.10d). A fifth student, Edwin, first collected all the green "baby worms" from his tablemates, and when he ran out, he asked them to share their blue "baby worms." Each "baby worm" was one inch long, and Edwin placed them end-to-end over the length of his forearm (see fig. 4.10e). When asked how long his arm was, he responded, "Eight!"

First and second graders generally have had more measurement experiences. Only the directions for task 14, exactly as written, were given to the first and second graders who were observed. No tools were suggested to the first graders; they could use the tool of their choice. The second graders, however, received a broken ruler and used only that tool to complete the task. The work of a first grader and a second grader are shown in figure 4.11.

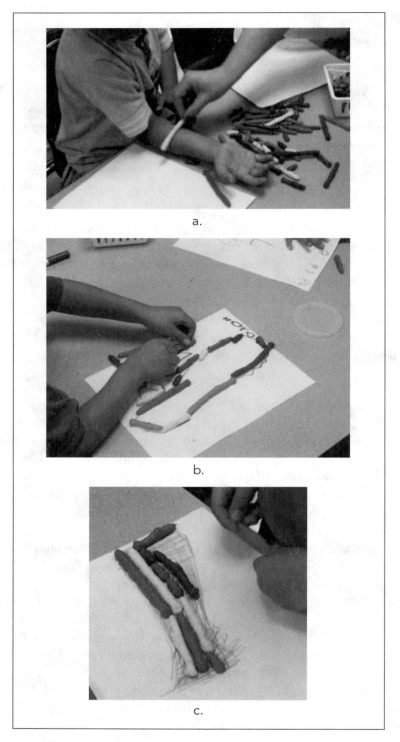

a.

b.

c.

Fig. 4.10. Prekindergartners' efforts to measure their forearms with soft plastic "worms" in one-inch, two-inch, three-inch, and four-inch lengths

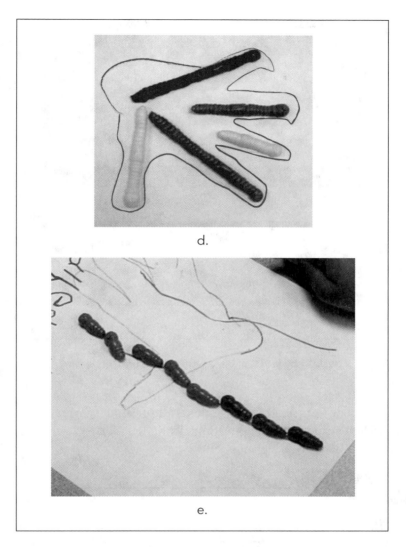

d.

e.

Fig. 4.10. *Continued*

Stephen, a first grader, was free to choose his own tool. Stephen made his measurement as shown in figure 4.11a, using a measuring tool made of one-inch straw sections in alternating colors, stiffened by a pipe cleaner threaded through it. The tool measured only seven inches; Stephen estimated that he needed one more inch for his measurement, added it to the seven inches, and said, "My forearm is eight inches." Jeremy, a second grader, worked with the broken ruler that he was given and measured as shown in figure 4.11b. The ruler began at two inches and ended at nine inches. Jeremy said, "The ruler should begin with zero, but I think you could do it. My forearm would be about ten inches 'cause that's seven inches, plus three more inches would make ten inches."

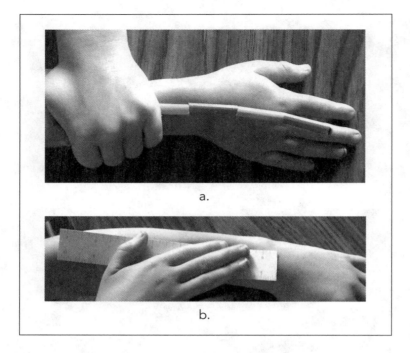

Fig. 4.11. Work on task 14 by (a) Stephen, a first grader, and (b) Jeremy, a second grader

Review the responses to task 14 from students in prekindergarten, first grade, and second grade. Then respond to the questions in Reflect 4.4.

Reflect 4.4

- **What did the students in prekindergarten, first grade, and second grade appear to understand or misunderstand as they responded to task 14? What difference did their experience levels appear to make in their responses?**

- **What activities do you think might have facilitated these students' continued development of Essential Understanding 4*a*?**

Clearly, not all the prekindergartners whose efforts are shown in figure 4.10 understood the attribute of length. Francisco measured the perimeter of his forearm, Amy measured the area of hers, and Kristen used the worms to mark the fingers on her hand. Mark appeared to start to measure the length of his arm, although he wanted to place the worms "side to side" rather than end-to-end. Francisco used the end-to-end method but measured the perimeter rather than the length of his forearm. Edwin appeared to understand the process of measuring length when he used same-sized units (all "baby worms," measuring one inch) and placed them end-to-end to measure the length that had been modeled by the teacher. However, when asked why he had used all "baby worms," he responded, "'Cause those are my favorites!" To extend and develop these students' understanding of the measurement process, the teacher might have asked them to analyze the number of worms that everyone used while wondering why everyone's number was so different from everyone else's. Using the smallest worms as the unit, they could have made one-inch length measurers with one-inch straw segments and pipe cleaners and used them in measurement experiments.

First and second graders have had many more measurement experiences than prekindergartners. Stephen and Jeremy, the first grader and second grader, respectively, whose work is shown in figure 4.11, measured their forearms by using two different types of length-measuring tools. The first graders had been using rulers made with one-inch sections of straws threaded with pipe cleaners. The length of the pipe cleaners limited the length of the measuring tool to seven inches. Stephen understood that he should place the measuring tool at his elbow, and when he was not able to get it all the way to his tallest finger, he estimated that the measurement needed just one more inch, thus obtaining a correct measurement of his forearm. Stephen's work suggests that he would have benefited from opportunities to compare his created measure with an inch ruler and explain how the numbers are used to label inches.

The second graders who completed the task with the broken ruler had previously had many experiences with conventional one-foot rulers. They generally had difficulty working on this task with the broken ruler. Jeremy was concerned that the ruler was not labeled correctly, and he informed the teacher of his concern several times, but he was still able to count the number of inches correctly, and then, using the knuckle of one of his fingers, he estimated three additional inches. When he was asked whether the result would be the same if he had a whole ruler, he expressed some uncertainty and then said that he should have had the whole ruler at the beginning, rather than the broken one. He did not fully understand that any point can serve as the origin, no matter what the label (that is, 0 to 7 would be the same length as 2 to 9). As Jeremy's work demonstrates, second graders need more experiences with broken rulers and opportunities to make the connection between the plastic-straw inch measurer used in first grade and the number labels on a ruler.

Task 15: Measuring in different units

Essential Understanding 4c captures a fundamental measurement concept related to units: "The size of the unit and the number of units in the measure are inversely related to each other." What activities might teachers offer to help their students develop this essential understanding? Think about this question before examining task 15, shown in figure 4.12. After examining the task, respond to the questions in Reflect 4.5.

Big Bill and Little Larry measured the width and length of the classroom, using feet. Big Bill said the room was 26 feet wide by 38 feet long. Little Larry said the room was 52 feet wide by 76 feet long. Why did Big Bill and Little Larry get different answers?

Measure your room's length and width, and tell why your solution is correct. Use measuring tools of your choice.

Fig. 4.12. Task 15

Reflect 4.5

- **What activities do you think might help students develop an understanding of the inverse relationship, captured in Essential Understanding 4c, between the size of the unit and the number of units in a measurement? How does task 15 address this essential understanding?**

- **What questions and comments do you think a teacher should use to help students understand the inverse relationship between the size of the unit and the number of units used to measure an attribute?**

Teachers should use problem-based inquiry activities to help students develop the important idea captured in Essential Understanding 4c that as the size of the unit used to measure increases, the number of those units in a measurement decreases, and vice versa. This inverse relationship is usually thought of as a concept that seven- or eight-year-olds may grasp but that younger children are not yet ready to understand. In fact, children can begin to develop this idea much earlier. For example, a group of prekindergartners were fascinated by Steve Jenkins's picture book *Actual Size* (2011), and they were particularly interested in the size of the foot of the largest land animal, the African elephant. The students had been measuring their heights by marking a line on cash register tape posted on the wall. Subsequently, the teacher added pictures of feet to the cash register tape so that students could count the numbers of feet that measured how tall they were. She used three different sizes of feet—baby feet, adult feet, and elephant feet—and allowed students to select how they wanted to be measured. Initially, many wanted to be measured in elephant feet, but when they realized they would only be two elephant feet tall, they quickly selected the baby feet!

Students in another kindergarten class were measuring themselves for a book that they were creating, "Life as a Kindergartner." One day they measured how tall they were, using a medium-sized paper teddy bear as the unit. The next day, they measured themselves again, this time using a small-sized paper teddy bear as the unit. In both cases, the teddy bears were arranged end-to-end on a totem pole that the students used as a measuring tool. They recorded both numbers, and when they were interviewed individually about the amazing increase in their number of teddy bears from the first measurement to the second, most of them responded with comments indicating that they believed that they had just "growed!" One student said, "My brother stretched me last night!" Another attributed the growth to "eating all my vegetables." What was more interesting, however, was that when a totem pole of very large bears was displayed, many students did not want to measure themselves with it, because "the big bears are not good!"

Task 15 was designed for first-grade students explicitly for the purpose of addressing this inverse relationship between the size of the unit and the number of units in a measurement. It was intended for use at the beginning of first grade because it dealt with a measurement concept rather than with a measurement skill—the skill of measuring length—something that students would learn in first grade. Its primary purpose was to assess whether a student could measure lengths accurately as well as demonstrate an understanding of the inverse relationship between the size of the unit and the number of units needed to measure that length.

The following is a partial script of a videotaped lesson using task 15, taught to rising first graders at the end of the kindergarten year. Pay attention to the teacher's comments and questions as well as the students' responses. This taped session lasted more than ninety minutes by student choice. In fact, the students wanted to keep working on the problem and continued the next day. Read the script and then respond to the questions in Reflect 4.6.

> *Setting:* Kindergarten classroom in May. The room was filled with boxes, and many materials were packed in preparation for a move to a new school. There were twenty-three students in the class.

Objective: To explore the relationship between the size of the unit (in this case, a foot) and the number of the units (or feet) needed to measure a specific length.

Lesson Procedures

1. Lesson problem was introduced and explained: "Big Bill and Little Larry measured the width and length of the classroom, using feet. Big Bill said the room was 26 feet by 38 feet. Little Larry said the room was 52 feet by 76 feet. Why did Big Bill and Little Larry get different answers?"

2. Students first discussed possible reasons for the difference with their partners. This discussion lasted approximately three minutes and was quite animated. The teacher then asked students to share their thoughts. The following were some of their remarks:

   - "Maybe Big Bill fell asleep and couldn't remember what he counted, so he made up a number."

   - "They could have counted different rooms."

   - "Big Bill could have forgotten how to count past 50, so he stopped when it got too hard."

   - "I think that since they are different, they get different numbers." Thinking that perhaps the student has some understanding here, the teacher checked with a question, "How are they different?" The student simply shrugged, and the teacher commented, "Yes, you are right. They do get different answers. The problem is Big Bill is big, and he gets little numbers, and Little Larry is little and he gets big numbers. I just don't get it!" Again, the student shrugged, and everyone in the class seemed to accept the whole situation as a real problem.

3. After about ten minutes of discussion, the teacher said, "Well, I need to know the answer, so I need you all to work with your partners and find out how big this room really is! The tools are over on the table, and you can use any tools you wish to solve this problem. Let's get to work!"

4. Students measured to find the real answer. Their behaviors were varied, but all the students were quite interested in measuring the room. The following were some of their actions:

   - A boy held a ruler and stepped sideways across the room while his partner counted the number of steps he made. When asked by the teacher to tell how the ruler helped him make the steps, he responded, "That's just how you measure!"

- A girl announced that the room was as "long as a stegosaurus!"

- Four children had measuring tapes strung completely across the room. When the teacher asked what they were doing, the children said that they needed "lots of measuring tapes to go all the way from one end to another." When the teacher asked, "How long is it?" group members discussed the matter and then looked at the last number on the tape and said "sixty" (the last number on one measuring tape). When the teacher asked, "Sixty what?" one student responded, "Sixty feet."

- A girl was hopping sideways, and her partner was counting numbers over a hundred when the teacher noticed and asked why she was hopping. She responded, "That's how you do all the feet!"

- A boy was lying on the floor and placing a ruler under a bookcase. When the teacher inquired what he was doing, he responded, "That's why they got different numbers . . . One went under the bookcases, and the other one didn't!"

- Many children were walking heel to toe from one end of the room to the other and counting each time they put a foot down.

5. After twenty minutes, students returned to the whole group to share their experiences. The teacher listened and recorded the partners' results, constantly asking questions and comparing students' results with those of Big Bill and Little Larry. When the students were finished, the teacher continued to present herself as puzzled and continued to ask how Big Bill and Little Larry could get different numbers. She kept looking at her own feet and motioning to show what a smaller foot would look like, and suddenly the students became excited and started to raise their hands. The comments were very different from those at the beginning of the lesson, but the teacher continued to comment, "I still don't get it! Big Bill is big, so I think he should have a big number. Little Larry is little, so he should have a little number!" Or she asked, "How are Little Larry's feet different from Big Bill's feet?" Some of their comments were as follows:

- "Big Bill's feet are big, so they take up more room. Little Larry's feet are little, and they don't take up as much room as Big Bill's, so you need more of them!"

- "Pretend that Big Bill has the biggest feet in the world, and he walked across the room in two giant feet . . . See, you wouldn't need as many of them as you would for Little Larry. Little Larry has really tiny feet [*motioning with hands to show feet of about three inches*], so you would need lots of these to get across the room . . . See?"

- "Yeah . . . I think the bigger the feet, the smaller the number, and the smaller the feet, the bigger the number."

6. After ninety minutes, the teacher asked the class to come up with the actual number of feet in the room, with the teacher's help.

Reflect 4.6

- **What does the conversation among the kindergartners recorded in the script suggest that they understood or misunderstood as they responded to task 15?**

- **What activities do you think the teacher could have offered these students to help them continue to develop their understanding of Essential Understanding 4c—the idea that the size of the unit used in measuring and the number of units in the measurement are inversely related to each other?**

The kindergartners' responses to this task are quite revealing. Initially, their answers to the question of why Big Bill and Little Larry came up with different measurements were creative but not based on any mathematical reasoning. As a result of their experiences during the lesson, their sharing of ideas, and their teacher's persistent pretense of confusion combined with her dispensing of strategic hints, the students began to understand that the size of the unit used and the number of units needed to measure are in a definite relationship. As they listened to the comments of their peers, they began to be able to reason about this relationship. However, they could have benefited from additional opportunities to measure other lengths two times, each time with a unit of a different size (for example, one time with inches and a second time with centimeters). Equally revealing are the processes that these kindergartners used to measure the room. The differences in their measuring techniques certainly point to the need for students to be explicitly taught the process of measuring and how to use specific tools and reason about different units.

Task 16: Measuring to collect science data

Task 16, shown in figure 4.13, was developed as part of a science unit on simple machines. Students experiment to see how far a sphere, a cylinder on its side, a cylinder on a base, and a rectangular prism will slide or roll when placed at the top of three different ramps—one with a height of 6 inches, a second with a height of 12 inches, and a third with a height of 24 inches. Although investigating the relationship of ramp height to distance traveled by an object placed on the ramp is a science goal, the task also offers rich possibilities for helping students meet mathematics standards related to geometry and measurement, providing them with a good opportunity to think about the attributes of shapes and the process of measuring length. Review task 16, and then respond to the questions in Reflect 4.7.

How far can the 3-D shapes shown below move (roll or slide) when released from the top of a ramp that is positioned at three different heights—6 inches, 12 inches, and 24 inches? Use any measuring tools of your choice. Record your results in the chart. Note that one shape—the cylinder—is oriented in two different ways for this task.

Height of ramp		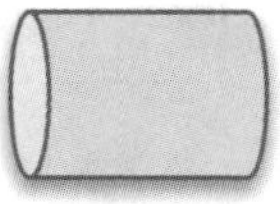		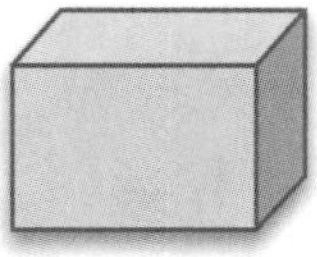
6 inches				
12 inches				
24 inches				

Fig. 4.13. Task 16

Reflect 4.7

- What evidence of Big Idea 4 and Essential Understandings 4a, 4b, 4c, and 4d might you expect to see as students complete task 16, an integrated mathematics and science task?

- Do you think that you could you assess students' understanding of the measurement process if you saw only their chart summaries? How might this process work?

Students in a second-grade class worked with partners, and, following instructions from their teacher, they used cash register tape to show how far each shape rolled. They labeled the strip of tape with the name of the shape as well as the height of the ramp. These second graders then measured the length of the cash register tape by using a tool of their choice. Results recorded digitally from two partner groups appear in figure 4.14 (an X indicates missing data). Examine these students' results, and then respond to the questions in Reflect 4.8.

	a. Partners: Joanie and Diana			
Height of ramp	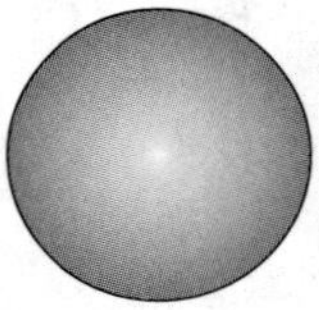	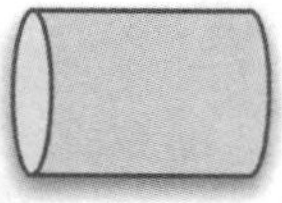		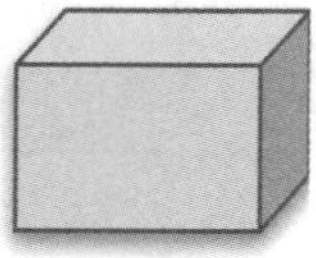
6 inches	5 R + ½ R	4 R	X	0
12 inches	7 R	Almost 6 R	X	0
24 inches	11 R + a little more	8 R	Almost 1 R	0

Fig. 4.14. Responses of two pairs of second graders, (a) Joanie and Diana and (b) John and Peter, to task 16

Height of ramp	sphere	cylinder (horizontal)	cylinder (vertical)	rectangular prism
6 inches	30 and 12	45 and 18	X	0
12 inches	70 and 29	50 and 20	X	X
24 inches	200 and 82	3 and 23	2 and 27	X

b. Partners: John and Peter

Fig. 4.14. *Continued*

Reflect 4.8

- Figure 4.14 shows results recorded by two pairs of second graders: (a) Joanie and Diana and (b) John and Peter. When you look at their completed charts, what questions do you think the teacher could have asked these students to help understand their answers?

- What evidence do you find in the charts of the students' understanding of measurement of geometric attributes?

Both pairs of students apparently placed the geometric solids correctly as indicated in the task because the shapes that moved down the ramp were the ones that might be classified as "rollers." In addition, both student pairs recorded numbers on the chart, showing that they understood the need to "specify 'how much' by assigning a number to such attributes as length" (Essential Understanding 4a). However, it is unclear what units these students used in their measurements. Joanie and Diana (see fig. 4.14a) incorporated into their answers the letter *R*, by which it is highly probable that they meant *ruler*. They may have measured the cash register tape by using multiple rulers or by using just one ruler, marking where it ended and repeating this process until they reached the end of the tape. In addition, with the exception of $\frac{1}{2}R$, they seemed to be unable to partition the ruler into parts because they used words rather than numbers to describe other parts of a whole, such as "a little more" or "almost."

By contrast, John and Peter (see fig. 4.14b) wrote two numbers for each length, presumably to represent each measurement in two different units, but they included no labels to indicate measurement units. The first number recorded may have represented the measurement in centimeters, and the second number may have represented the measurement in inches. In some cases, that relationship seems to make sense. In fact, these students were using a ruler with inches marked on one edge and centimeters on the other, so they may easily have measured first with the centimeter edge and then with the inch edge. The difficulty is accounting for their measurements for the cylinder on its side and the cylinder on its base with the ramp set at a height of 24 inches. The numbers 3 and 23, given for the cylinder on its side on this ramp, do not make sense under the same interpretation as the measurements for the sphere and this same cylinder on the lower ramps. Even if John and Peter switched the numbers by mistake, 23 centimeters and 3 inches do not indicate the same length. An alternative explanation is possible: The rulers that the students were using had the zero at opposite ends for centimeters and inches, with the numbers 23 and 3 across from each other on the ruler. So perhaps John and Peter forgot to turn the ruler around after measuring inches or centimeters. Whatever the case, without labels for the unit, it is difficult to understand the measurements.

Summarizing Pedagogical Content Knowledge to Support Big Idea 4 through Essential Understandings 4a–4d

Teaching the mathematical ideas in this chapter requires specialized knowledge related to the four components presented in the Introduction: learners, curriculum, instructional strategies, and assessment. The four sections that follow summarize some examples of these specialized knowledge bases in relation to Essential Understandings 4a, 4b, 4c, and 4d. Although we separate them to highlight their importance we also recognize that they are connected and support one another.

Knowledge of learners

Measurement is indeed a complex combination of concepts and skills. This chapter's samples of students' work and descriptions of their behaviors and responses to tasks 13–16 provide many examples of common understandings and misunderstandings about concepts and skills related to measurement. Three characteristics of early learners have been especially evident in this chapter:

1. Young students need many varied measuring experiences.

2. Young students are purposefully involved in learning about measurements and the process of measuring.

3. Young students' growth of understanding of the measurement of length and the significance of the unit follows a developmental progression.

It is worth considering each of these characteristics with respect to the sample responses to the tasks in Chapter 4.

First, the varied examples in the chapter have underscored how important it is for young students to have many different experiences in measurement. The samples of student work come from teachers and other observers in public, private, and home schools, some in high-needs settings, in various states. In all cases, how students approached these tasks depended on their prior experiences with measurement.

Many of these young students appeared to have acquired some procedural measurement skills, some correct and some incorrect. They had often picked up several "rules," such as, "You cannot start with the 2 on a ruler" or "Count the numbers on both sides of the ruler and write both numbers" (see fig. 4.14b). However, they sometimes did not understand what attribute they were measuring, why they were measuring, what unit they are using, the concepts of conservation or transitivity, or the need for equal-sized units in a measurement.

In addition to revealing which students had, and which students had not had, prior experience with some measurement "rules" or procedures, the students' approaches to the tasks made clear who was familiar with measuring tools and who was not. When Jeremy (fig. 4.11b) measured the length of his forearm by combining a measurement made with a broken ruler with a measurement made by using the length of his knuckle, he was demonstrating his prior experience with a ruler and with an informal tool that helped him estimate inches. He was able to use both tools correctly. By contrast, students with less experience with rulers simply recorded numbers when both inches and centimeters were marked, not fully understanding what the numbers in the measurement represented.

Second, while students were engaged in the measuring tasks discussed in Chapter 4, they were purposefully involved and motivated. They wanted to know which one was taller, which held more, which covered more, or how many special square corners they could find. They were eager to see how long their forearms were (task 14), to measure the length and width of the room correctly (task 15), or to find out which three-dimensional shape traveled the farthest on one of the ramps (task 16). They willingly experimented with measuring tools. Their classroom interactions regarding measurement were mostly helpful and cooperative, and they were heard to say, for example, "Let me show you," or "I have used this one before." The comments that they shared in whole-class and one-on-one discussions were sometimes thoughtful—for instance, "The big feet take up more room so you don't need as many." And their conversations included increasingly precise measurement vocabulary, such as "longer," "taller," and "covers more," rather than the much more general and less precise "bigger." Just as important, this more precise vocabulary frequently made its way into other places besides mathematics classes.

Third, learners generally demonstrated the developmental progression of under-standing of length measurement outlined by Clements and Sarama (2009, p. 169–72). An abridged progression is shown in the chart in figure 4.15, which also pro-vides a few examples from this chapter. The age categories are listed by grade level because students' precise ages were usually unknown.

The three characteristics of early learners with respect to measurement discussed above—developing understanding through many and varied experiences, demon-strating purposeful involvement and high motivation, and learning in a develop-mental progression—are clearly relevant to the topics discussed in sequence below: curriculum, instructional strategies, and assessment.

Knowledge of curriculum

Although the essential understandings identified for pre-K–grade 2 teachers by Goldenberg and Clements (2014) approach measurement quite broadly, only length measurement is addressed in the standards set out for K–grade 2 students in the Common Core State Standards (National Governors Association Center for Best Practices and Council of Chief State School Officers [NGA Center and CCSSO] 2010). Essential Understanding 4a specifically mentions the measurable attributes of "length, area, volume, and angle" for geometric shapes. The tasks presented in this chapter that involve area, volume, and angle illustrate the range of experiences that are important for developing this understanding and can be useful in specific cases for developing understanding of other mathematics content as well. For example, when comparing the areas of tangram shapes in subtask 13e (see fig. 4.7), students could have used grids as structures to compare the space covered by the tangram shapes (in an approach similar to that taken in subtask 6e in Chapter 2; see fig. 2.6). When they were comparing the volumes of "mystery" boxes in response to subtask 13d, they were also meeting an important number standard as they counted by hundreds and tens and combined these counts to find the total number of cubes.

Grade level	Stage in developmental progression	Example
Pre-K	• Identifies length/distance as attribute and compares length directly • Compares the length of two objects by representing them with a third object • May assign a number to a length but ignores the starting point and the need for equal-sized units	• Students' direct comparison of tower heights (see fig. 4.4a and accompanying discussion, p. 104) • Students' use of a pipe cleaner to go around the fruits to compare them (see fig. 4.3a) • Anthony's drawing of himself and his teacher (see fig. 4.1b); Francisco's measuring of the length of his forearm (fig. 4.10b)
K	• Lays units end-to-end to measure length	• Francisco's and Edwin's placement of the measuring worms (figs. 4.10b and 4.10e)
Grade 1	• Repeats units to measure lengths • Relates size and number of units explicitly	• Stephen's use of his straw inch measurer (fig. 4.11a) • Older kindergartners' thinking about Big Bill's and Little Larry's measurements (see script, pp. 121–24, related to task 15)
Grade 2	• Measures, understanding need for identical units, relationship between different units, partitions of unit, zero point on rulers, and accumulation of distance	• Students' counts of numbers of rulers or inches and centimeters (figs. 4.14a and 4.14b), disregarding their omission of unit labels

Fig. 4.15. Developmental progression for length measurement
(Clements and Sarama 2009), paired with age-appropriate examples

When they were comparing angles that were or were not "special square corners," students were also gaining a better understanding of a defining attribute of rectangles. Regardless of the curriculum in use, measurement activities should address more than concepts and skills related to length measurement.

Measuring tools are another important component of curriculum. The tasks in this chapter use a large variety of tools—many that provide standard units of measure and some that present units that would be considered nonstandard. Typically, teachers of young students use tools with nonstandard units first and then progress to tools with standard units. Current research (see Clements and Sarama 2009, pp. 166–67) indicates that the use of nonstandard tools can be confusing to young students. The tools that students appear to prefer and understand best are standard tools, such as rulers and measuring tapes, or tools that can be directly related to standard tools, such as the measuring worms used in task 14 by prekindergartners to find the length of their forearms (see fig. 4.10) or the tool consisting of connected one-inch straw segments used by Stephen for the same task (see fig. 4.11a).

With these findings in mind, carefully consider the tools that you use. For example, think about the fact that measuring tapes typically have inches labeled on one edge and centimeters labeled on the other so that users can read the measurement from either the centimeter side or the inch side. However, rulers typically show inches increasing from one end and centimeters increasing from the opposite end, allowing students to see two sets of numbers at one time, one of which does not give the measurement that they intend to make. This confusion was evident in tasks in which students recorded two numbers to measure a length and were uncertain about how to label the units or how to measure accurately (see the discussion of students' comparisons of the tower heights in subtask 13b [fig. 4.4] and John and Peter's measurements of three-dimensional objects' movements down ramps in task 16 [fig. 4.14b]).

Because measurement has so many practical, real-life applications, any curriculum should be designed to apply the related skills and concepts. These applications seem obvious and could be easily integrated in other content areas besides mathematics—especially science and technology. Task 16, in which students explore the movement of three-dimensional objects on ramps of different heights, is a good example of a task that addresses both science and mathematics learning. Even an activity as simple as comparing the capacities of containers (subtask 13c) develops ideas in both science and mathematics. Measurement also has a variety of at-home applications as well as connections to physical education and social studies. It is a perfect topic to use to bring together all areas of learning while motivating young students.

Consider the information in this chapter and how it relates to the curriculum that you use. Think about your curriculum (including textbooks, materials, tools, and technology) and how it supports instruction related to Essential Understandings 4a–4d. Evaluate how your curriculum emphasizes these essential understandings and decide whether you need to (1) continue to use all or part of it, (2) adapt some of the tasks so that they emphasize a different approach, or (3) create new tasks to address these ideas. Ask yourself the following questions:

- How is length measurement introduced and developed in the curriculum? Does the curriculum focus primarily on procedures, or does it involve concepts related to measurement?

- Are students measuring the attributes of items in hands-on activities, or are they looking at illustrations in a textbook (for example, an illustration of a pencil with a ruler below it)?

- Are students introduced to concepts related to measuring area, volume, and angle? Does the curriculum include any activities that ask them to compare area, volume, or angles by using physical objects?

- What tools does the curriculum expect students to use to measure? Do tasks use a variety of standard tools? How are the nonstandard tools directly related to standard tools?

- What real-life applications of measurement does the curriculum suggest? Does it include opportunities to integrate content from other subject areas?

Knowledge of instructional strategies

Three strategies are fundamental to support instruction in measurement with young learners:

1. Creating an environment that *over time* helps students develop measurement concepts

2. Asking open-ended questions and creating opportunities to listen to students' thinking and letting them listen to the thinking of others

3. Modeling measurement procedures explicitly in the context of everyday experiences

Again, considering these in turn can be very useful.

First, throughout this chapter, suggestions to facilitate students' understanding have included offering more experiences over time. Unfortunately, teachers do not have enough time to teach everything, and, for various reasons, measurement and geometry are often the last topics addressed in the school year. In addition, measurement is generally taught as a self-contained unit rather than something that needs to be taught and learned over time. For these reasons, it is important to create an environment in which you can provide your students with measurement experiences throughout the school year. You can do this by creating a measurement center, offering a specific measurement task in the center every week or two, and debriefing your students in small groups. You should be sure that the tasks are sequenced developmentally and that you offer a measurement focus activity every month that provides concentrated time on length or area problems, or even a measurement project that is part of a science or technology curriculum. Most of the samples of student work in this chapter were produced in measurement centers or as responses to focus activities that were used within everyday classes.

Second, asking open-ended questions is essential for supporting mathematical thinking at every level. The script of the kindergartners' efforts to explain the differences between Big Bill's and Little Larry's measurements in task 15 (see pp. 120–24) shows how a teacher very effectively implements a strategy of posing open-ended questions, offering strategic comments, listening closely to her students' thinking, and encouraging them to listen carefully to her thinking and one another's. Often, this teacher says, "Listen to me think," before stating a common misconception or an idea that is only partially correct. She states a common misconception as her own: "I still don't get it! Big Bill is big, so I think he should have a big number. Little Larry is little, so he should have a little number!" In fact, she explicitly states this misconception many times over the course of the class, pretending to be confused or perplexed each time, while also looking at her own feet and motioning to show what a smaller foot would look like. Finally, the students become excited as they begin to understand that the size of the unit is inversely related to the number of units needed to measure a length. Posing open-ended questions as well as encouraging students to listen as the teacher thinks aloud are good strategies for facilitating understanding.

Third, teachers model measuring almost every day in the classroom, outdoors, or in other places inside the school where students go during the day. Measuring the area of a learning center table if another desk is joined to it, measuring the distance that students travel to come in from recess when they are in the soccer field, or filling a file box with more and more materials and hoping to have enough room for everything are all examples of everyday measuring. Students model what their teachers do, and if we talk aloud to ourselves as we measure, we make the procedures, as well as the concepts, more explicit, and, in so doing, we have an opportunity to increase student learning.

These three instructional strategies are just a few of the many that could be used to build young students' understanding of measurement. But assessment is closely aligned with curriculum and instruction and must be considered as well.

Knowledge of assessment

Almost all the responses from students presented in this chapter offer opportunities to assess the students' understanding of measurement. Some of the strategies that might be used for assessments are identified in the chart in figure 4.16, which lists corresponding examples discussed in the chapter.

Remember that the assessment strategies emphasized throughout the chapters in this book are intended to inform instruction and that assessment should occur at three points:

Assessment strategy	Occasion for using strategy	Location of example in chapter
Listening to conversations	• Students discussing transitivity • Students discussing conservation	See conversations between Asa and Joey (p. 98) and Mandy and Beth (p. 99).
Making "so if . . ." comments regarding a student's response	• Teacher saying, "So if this is the container that holds the most water, what would happen when . . ."	See dialogue among teacher and students in subtask 13c (pp. 106–7).
Observing students' reactions when they can't find the words to express themselves	• Prekindergartner using his finger to model a vertical orientation • Students' demonstrating misconceptions about the use of decomposing shapes to compare	See discussion of side-by-side towers composed of different numbers of blocks (p. 104 and fig. 4.4a). See students' work with tangram pieces (p. 109 and fig 4.7).
Asking questions after a response	• Teacher asking students what made specific angles *not* "special square corners"	See discussion of subtask 13f (p. 110–11) and students' difficulty in finding angles that were not "special square corners."
Analyzing written work from another class without having the opportunity to ask any other questions	• Evaluating students' responses on chart recording distances traveled by 3-D shapes down a ramp	See Joanie and Diana's work (fig. 4.14a) and John and Peter's work (fig. 4.14b).

Fig. 4.16. Strategies for assessing students' understanding of measurement in pre-K–grade 2

1. *Before* a lesson is taught, to gauge what students already know or what their partial understanding includes

2. *During* a lesson, to determine how to adapt instruction in real time

3. *After* a lesson, to evaluate what students have learned

Instruction can improve *only if* the teacher knows what students understand, what they do not understand, and how to facilitate their learning to understand.

Conclusion

This chapter has presented four different tasks to show how young learners understand measurement, especially in relation to the measurement of geometric attributes. These tasks are designed to illustrate ways in which teachers of young students can engage them in making size comparisons with respect to the attributes of length, area, volume, and angle (task 13), measuring length (task 14), investigating the relationship between unit size and number of units in a measurement (task 15), and using measuring skills to report the distances traveled by objects down ramps of different lengths (task 16). The next chapter introduces some activities that deal with the often-neglected topic of transforming shapes and space and thinking about what changes and what does not change. Such activities are typically challenging but can also be great fun!

practice

Chapter 5
Transforming Space and Objects

Big Idea 3
We gain insight and understanding of spaces and the objects within them by noting what does and does not change as we transform these spaces and objects in various ways.

Essential Understanding 3*a*
Transformations can be used to describe differences between an idealized image of an object and the way that it is positioned in space or seen by the eye.

Essential Understanding 3*b*
Under each transformation, certain properties are invariant.

This chapter focuses on tasks that put into practice concepts related to transformations as presented in *Developing Essential Understanding of Geometry and Measurement for Teaching Mathematics in Prekindergarten–Grade 2* (Goldenberg and Clements 2014). Big Idea 3 of geometry and measurement and its associated understandings capture the concept of transformation and point to the relationship of transformation to other ideas.

Working toward Big Idea 3 through Essential Understandings 3*a* and 3*b*

Previous chapters have focused on helping students develop their understanding of classifying shapes (Chapter 1), structuring space to identify an object's location (Chapter 2), decomposing and composing shapes (Chapter 3), and comparing and measuring geometric attributes (Chapter 4). Chapter 5 now uses the ideas from these earlier chapters and discusses how to guide young students in understanding objects that they see in space directly in front of them, reflections in mirrors, enlarged images of objects, or, sometimes, images that have been distorted in some way.

The chapter shows how to help students gain insight into or *discover* (a more appropriate term for young learners) what changes and what does not change when transformations occur. Goldenberg and Clements's (2014) goal is to give *teachers* the ideas and understanding of these topics that they need to be effective in their work with students, whereas our goal is to show teachers how to give *students* the understanding that they need to be successful as they grow in learning. Consequently, this chapter does not address all the ideas that Goldenberg and Clements share or present the ideas as fully and formally as they do. It is appropriate that young students learn about this topic informally and investigate the changes that occur, or do not occur, when familiar objects are transformed. The Common Core State Standards for Mathematics (CCSSM; National Governors Association Center for Best Practices and Council of Chief State School Officers [NGA Center and CCSSO] 2010) suggest introducing symmetry to students as a formal mathematical idea in fourth grade (4.G.3) and recommend addressing other transformation terms and concepts more formally in eighth grade (8.G.1, 8.G.2, 8.G.3, 8.G.4).

In focusing on an informal early approach to transformations, Chapter 5 examines four transformation tasks. Continuing the numbering from the previous chapters, these are tasks 17–20. In task 17, young students see two-dimensional shapes placed in relationship to each other in a photograph (or on a magnetic board or in some other format). Then the photograph (or other visual display) is removed, and the students try to replicate what they saw. In task 18, students experiment with mirrors, placing them on two-dimensional shapes to see how the shapes can be transformed in reflections. Task 19 extends task 18 by asking students to identify objects that when folded or reflected on a "line of symmetry" are divided into two halves that are identical to each other. Task 20 engages students in creating all the unique objects that they can when five cubes are connected. Students will need to see the creations in many orientations before they can label them as *unique*. Before examining each of these four tasks, however, consider some general comments about young students and what they are likely to know or not know.

First, young students are likely to be very familiar with the term *transform* or *transformer* because of recent popular movies and toys. When preschool students were asked to transform a clay sphere into a cylinder, they understood what was meant, and, with a little work, they made a model of a shape that "looked like a pipe." When they were asked what changed, they responded, "There are flat parts now," or "It rolls long."

Second, prekindergarten students can generally identify a shape in any orientation. For example, if they know that a triangle is a triangle when it looks like

,

they know that it is a triangle if it looks like

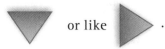

This certainty seems to weaken, however, when young students are introduced to letters in the alphabet—specifically, b, d, p, and q—because they learn that the orientation of the letter changes the name and sound of the letter. When kindergarten students were asked to identify a triangle in different orientations, they often responded that

is a triangle, but these are not:

When asked why each of these was not a triangle, they responded that the shape did not "look right" or was "a duck beak" or was "upside down." One student responded that the "upside down" triangle should "look like a girl." When asked why he said that, the student showed a door that had a circle and a "good triangle" under it to identify the girl's bathroom!

The tasks that Chapter 5 presents are open-ended and discovery-based. Generally, they provide opportunities for teachers to gain insight into students' understanding of transformation and for students to observe what is different and what is the same when an object is transformed in space. Additionally, these tasks provide students with opportunities to look at the specific properties of shapes that do not vary, or are *invariant*.

Task 17: Look, make, fix

Task 17, shown in figure 5.1, has three steps: look, make, fix. Students look at a shape composed of tangram pieces. Then, with the shape covered or out of view, they try to re-create it, using tangram pieces. When they are finished, they look again at the shape and fix their replication. Review Task 17, and respond to the questions in Reflect 5.1. Think about specific geometric properties that are involved in this task, as well as the relationships among the component shapes in the task.

Play "Look, Make, and Fix," using tangram shapes. Use photographs 1 and 2 below, which show different shape compositions with tangram pieces.

Give the students one of the photos, and have them move through the Look-Make-Fix steps below:

Look: Look at the photograph.

Make: Hide the photograph. Make the shape composition that you saw in it with tangram pieces so that your creation looks just like the one in the photograph that you saw.

Fix: Take the photo from its hiding place and look at it again. Fix your tangram composition to look just like the one in the photograph.

Photograph 1

Photograph 2

Fig. 5.1. Task 17

Reflect 5.1

- How does task 17 relate to transformation and the essential understandings that this chapter addresses?

- What specific geometric properties would you expect students to replicate well? Where would you expect them to have difficulty?

The shape in photograph 1 and that in photograph 2 were chosen because of their properties—both are bilaterally symmetrical and both are familiar symbols to children (an arrow and an evergreen tree). Figure 5.2 shows the responses of prekindergarten students who were sitting in rows on the floor and looking at the teacher's magnetic board on which she made these two shapes with magnetic tangram pieces. The magnetic board was a short distance from the students (2 meters at the most) and slightly higher than their eye level. They had to replicate the shapes as "seen by the eye," and when they fixed their re-creations, they had to describe how their shape differed from the one that they saw on the teacher's board (Essential Understanding 3*a*). Review the sample responses shown in figure 5.2 and respond to the questions in Reflect 5.2 regarding the students' replications of the model. A word of caution: Do not underestimate the abilities of young students to do this task. Teachers often express surprise when students who typically have difficulty with number activities are able to complete the task easily. And sometimes students

Fig. 5.2. Four prekindergartners' responses to task 17

Reflect 5.2

- **On the basis of the responses in figure 5.2, what do you think the prekindergartners appeared to understand or misunderstand in the transformation activity in task 17?**

- **What types of shapes would you use to facilitate and extend these students' understanding after they were successful at this task?**

who usually do more traditional mathematics tasks with ease struggle with this activity.

All the prekindergarten students whose work is shown in figure 5.2 understood the task, selected the correct shapes, and used the correct number of shapes, with the exception of Kaylee, who used a square rather than a triangle in her re-creation of the shape in photograph 2. Further, all students placed the shapes in the correct relationship in their replications of the arrangements in both photographs. The misunderstanding that occurred involved the size of the different triangles used. When the students analyzed their arrangements and explained the differences, most of them did not recognize the disparities in the sizes of the triangles selected. They could identify differences in size only when they physically matched the shapes shown in the photographs with their shapes. To develop and extend the thinking of such students, you could provide more examples of symmetrical shapes composed of triangles of different sizes and use pictures that are not symmetrical.

Task 18: Mirror reflection

Task 18, shown in figure 5.3, draws young students' attention to the shape-making possibilities of mirror reflections. Students are given four shapes—a rectangle, a triangle, a circle, and a hexagon—and they work with a small rectangular mirror to reflect all or part of each to make new shapes. This task was given to students in a multi-age, pre-K–grade 2 classroom. Students of different ages worked together at tables and were encouraged to interact with one another as they worked. Previously, they had experimented with mirrors and reflections of objects, animals, and people, all represented in photographs. They had also learned how to place the longest edge of the mirror in various places on the photographs to see different reflections. They used the same procedures in task 18 to create new shapes from the two-dimensional shapes pictured. Consider the questions in Reflect 5.3, and, as you formulate your responses, think about the information in previous chapters as well as the information in this chapter.

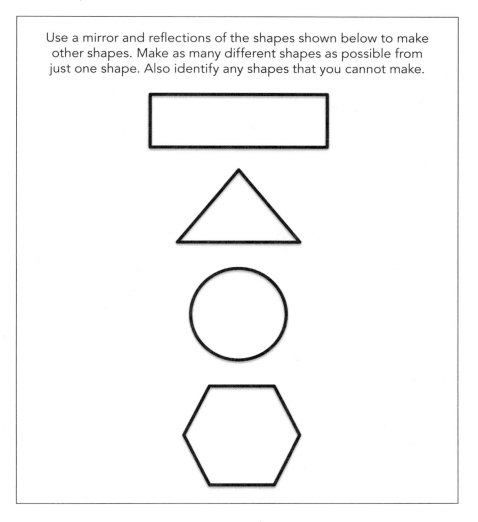

Use a mirror and reflections of the shapes shown below to make other shapes. Make as many different shapes as possible from just one shape. Also identify any shapes that you cannot make.

Fig. 5.3. Task 18

Reflect 5.3

- How does task 18, shown in figure 5.3, support the development of the essential understandings addressed in this chapter? What essential understandings addressed in other chapters are also relevant to this task?

- What vocabulary might you expect students to use as they work on this task?

As they work with mirrors in this task, students will create shapes that combine a reflected part of one of the pictured shapes with part of the original shape. Big Idea 3 and Essential Understandings 3*a* and 3*b* are addressed as students view mirror images and note properties that do or do not change from the original shape to the new shape. Essential understandings associated with Big Idea 1 also come into play as students describe the new shapes in relation to the original shapes—and students may draw on other essential understandings as well. Vocabulary regarding shape, size, and orientation will enter into the conversations as students interact with one another.

Figure 5.4 shows a sampling of students' responses to the task but does not really do justice to them. Conversations could not be recorded in their entirety, nor could the students' excitement be registered. "Look what I found!" and "Has anyone got a quadrilateral yet?" and "What's the name of that shape?" erupted in the classroom, and many of the students' comments and pictures could not be included. In fact, when students were asked at the end of the class period what shapes could *not* be made with the mirrors and shapes provided, several students said that they thought they could make *every* shape if they had enough time! Review the responses in figure 5.4. Note that the arrows and mirror lines were added by the scribe to indicate where the student placed the mirror. After examining the students' work, respond to the questions in Reflect 5.4.

Reflect 5.4

- Examine the responses to task 18 shown in figure 5.4. What did the students appear to understand or misunderstand as they explored the idea of reflections in this task?

- What mathematical vocabulary did students use to discuss their created shapes?

All the students understood what to do in the task, and they were eager to place the mirror so that they could discover the reflected shapes. The vocabulary that they used indicated understandings related to classification of shapes (Chapter 1) and spatial orientation (Chapter 2), and, in many cases, they used very precise and accurate language in describing the transformations. Some of their statements also indicated emerging ideas related to Essential Understandings 3*a* and 3*b*. The students revealed an awareness of the fact that the shape changed in some reflections

Shape and placement of mirror (arrow shows direction in which reflective surface is facing)	Comments overheard as students worked on the task
	"I can make a longer one." "Me too! I can even make it longer by just moving [the mirror]."
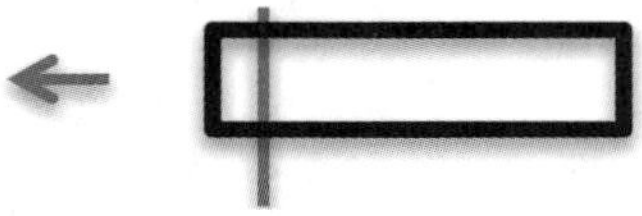	"I made a square . . . Not a rectangle." "A rectangle *is* a square . . . Remember? It's just special."
	"I can even make a square by putting the mirror on the corner—see?"
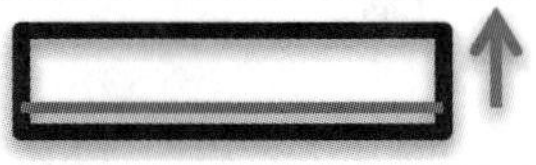	"I can make a fat rectangle if I put it longways."
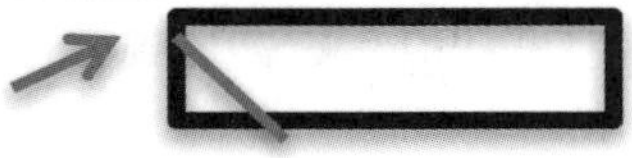	"I made a hexagon . . . like an arrow by putting it right here [*motioning where it is*]. It's gotta be in the corner." "*Square* corner?" [*Students noticed teacher was taking notes.*] "Yeah . . . Show-off!"
	"Look at this one . . . When it's in the middle, I get the same shape as I started with . . ."
	"Same shape again . . . I can put the mirror one way or the other, and I still get the same thing!"
	"I just made a little diamond . . . Or a crooked square!"
	"I made a bow tie! What's it called?" "Count the sides." "Six sides! That's an octagon, I think!"
	"Looks kinda like a football!" "Yeah, the circle is boring!" "Let's stick with the other ones . . ."
	"If you put the mirror on opposite corners, you always get the same shape again no matter what way the mirror is facing!" [*From a second grader*]

Fig. 5.4. Responses from students in a multi-age classroom to task 18

("I made a hexagon" or "I made a bow tie!") and that it stayed the same in other reflections ("When it's in the middle, I get the same shape I started with!" or "Same shape again"). As the students noted, they did not have enough time to find all the shapes that they could make. Their teacher decided to make this task a challenge for interested students, and a class chart was made in which students could record new shapes that they discovered as well as discoveries of ones that they thought were impossible to make with a reflection.

Task 19: Exploring symmetry

Task 19, shown in figure 5.5, offers an early exploration of the important geometric idea of symmetry. Before offering this task, you might introduce students to the term *symmetry* by using and building on the vocabulary that they used in their work on task 18. In that task, students investigate shapes that "stay the same" when mirrors are placed in "the middle." Reflect on the connections between tasks 18 and 19 and their relationship to Essential Understandings 3*a* and 3*b*. Use the questions in Reflect 5.5 to guide you in considering some of the instructional implications of exploring symmetry with young students.

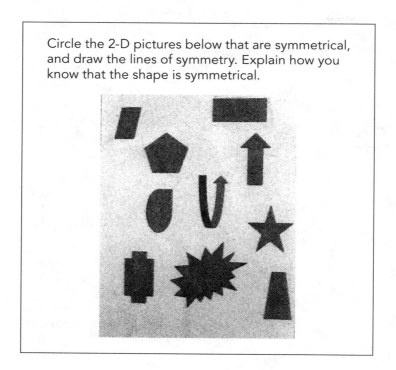

Fig. 5.5. Task 19

Reflect 5.5

- Why does it make sense to introduce the idea of symmetry to students in pre-K–grade 2?

- What strategies would you suggest that a teacher use to facilitate students' understanding of symmetry?

The two samples of student work included in figure 5.6 give a suggestion of what young students can understand and do, as well as the growth of more sophisticated ideas about symmetry with age and experience. A kindergartner's work is shown in (a), and a second grader's work appears in (b). Both students worked in crayon; heavier lines were drawn over the crayon lines later to make them more visible.

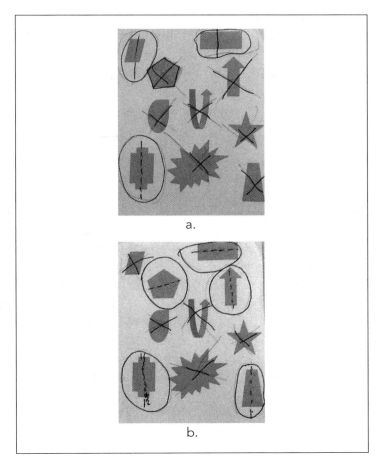

Fig. 5.6. Responses from two students,
(a) a kindergartner and (b) a second grader, to task 19

When the kindergartner whose work appears in in figure 5.6a was asked to explain his reasoning for his responses, he asked for scissors and another copy of the task. He attempted to cut out the shapes that he had marked as symmetrical so that he could fold them and demonstrate their symmetry. When his strategy did not work for the quadrilateral shown in the upper left corner, he attributed the difficulty to his inexact cutting and said, "You just need to look, and you know!" When the second grader was asked to explain her reasoning (see fig. 5.6b), she simply pointed to the symmetrical shapes that she had identified and said that both sides were exactly the same, and she modeled with a mirror as she explained her decisions. When asked whether other lines of symmetry were possible, she responded, "No." Review the two students' work and respond to the questions in Reflect 5.6.

Reflect 5.6

- Examine the samples of student work shown in figure 5.6. What symmetrical shapes did the students identify correctly? What symmetrical shapes did they identify incorrectly? How would you assess their understanding or misunderstanding?

- How do you think asking these students to explain their work contributed to their understanding?

Both students correctly classified five shapes: the razor blade, the long rectangle, the teardrop, the curved arrow, and the starburst. Of these, they correctly named the razor blade and the long rectangle as symmetrical (they identified different lines of symmetry in the rectangle) and correctly identified the teardrop, the curved arrow, and the starburst as not symmetrical. In addition, both incorrectly classified the five-pointed star as not symmetrical. These students marked each of four remaining shapes—the upper-left quadrilateral (parallelogram), the pentagon, the up-arrow, and the lower right quadrilateral (isosceles trapezoid)—differently, with the second grader identifying all four correctly (all symmetrical except the parallelogram) and the kindergartner identifying all four incorrectly. The kindergartner did not see three of the shapes as symmetrical although they were, and he saw one of the shapes (the upper-left quadrilateral) as symmetrical although it was not.

Although the second grader misidentified only one shape in the group (the five-pointed star), she did not yet understand that a shape may have more than one line of symmetry. Her explanations of her answers were generally strong; however, she clearly needed additional experiences to help her discover that more than one line of symmetry may be possible in a shape. The kindergartner's responses indicated that he had some understanding of the meaning of symmetry. Because he had difficulty cutting the small shapes accurately, his previously successful strategy of folding and matching symmetrical shapes did not always work for him this time. Although he was unable to apply his strategy to demonstrate symmetry for the quadrilateral in the upper-left corner, he believed that the problem was with his cutting rather than with his idea that the shape was symmetrical: "You just need to look, and you know!" Further, the lines that he drew suggest that he may have thought that symmetrical lines can be drawn only down the middle of a shape, from top to bottom. Unfortunately, that isn't always true!

Task 20: Exploring all the unique five-cube creations

The last task in this chapter—and the book—is task 20, shown in figure 5.7. Intended as a group task for second graders, this task requires students to work with five connecting cubes and form all the unique creations using all five cubes. The challenge in this task is to take into account all the various ways in which the creations can be positioned in space in order to identify and eliminate duplicates. Students' understanding of transformations can help them solve the problem. Review the task and respond to the questions in Reflect 5.7.

Work with five connecting cubes, and make all the different five-cube creations that are possible. A shape is considered the same as another shape if it can be moved in any way to make it exactly the same as the other shape. Reflections are sometimes considered to be different creations. Consider reflections as different in this task.

Examples:
These two shapes are the same even though they are oriented differently, with one standing vertically and one lying horizontally:

(continued on page 150)

Fig. 5.7. Task 20

These three shapes are the same even though they are oriented differently:

These two shapes are reflections of each other; they are different creations:

Fig. 5.7. *Continued*

Reflect 5.7

- Examine task 20 in figure 5.7. How do you think the task would help students "describe differences between an idealized image of an object and the way it is positioned in space or seen by the eye?" (Essential Understanding 3*a*)

- What instructional strategies might you employ to facilitate students' discussions about the different compositions of five cubes?

As students create shapes in task 20, they have to consider how five cubes can be connected to each other to make *new* creations—not ones that they already have. As students try to make the complete set of unique five-cube creations, they must be constantly on the lookout for duplicate creations. To do this, they must mentally identify those creations that appear similar and then maneuver each one physically to see whether it matches another one in their set. To succeed in this work, students benefit from talking with their peers after comparing what they see from different viewpoints. Instructionally, this points to the advantage of using a variety of grouping procedures to allow students to obtain many different viewpoints. The process that was used in one second-grade classroom was as follows:

1. The task was presented to the class, and the students worked together in groups of four to create as many unique combinations as possible.

2. The groups reviewed other groups' creations *without touching them*. They then returned to their own creations and used the information they had gleaned from their visual review to add to or discard creations.

3. All the groups displayed their creations in the classroom for one week so that everyone could analyze the cube creations (see fig. 5.8). At this point, students were allowed to maneuver the creations physically to see whether they matched other creations, and again groups could add to or discard their own creations as needed.

4. Groups then compared their creations to drawings of all the unique five-cube creations (see fig. 5.9), added to or discarded their own creations, and discussed their final creations.

Fig. 5.8. One group's set of five-cube creations on display in the classroom

Before all the groups discussed their final sets of five-cube creations, each group responded to a questionnaire about their creation process. The whole class then met to discuss the all the groups' final creations and share thinking. The following are some of their responses to the questions on the questionnaire:

•   How did you decide to organize your creations so that you would not duplicate any shape?

Fig. 5.9. Drawings of the twenty-nine unique cube creations (Copley 1998)

- ○ "At first, we didn't organize them . . . We just made them, and we had lots of the same ones."
- ○ "We put all the ones that had five cubes touching the table in one place, then four cubes touching the table, and then only three cubes touching the table. Sometimes that worked but not always."

- ○ "We decided to have an inspector, and that person picked one and kept looking and turning shapes."
- How did you make new creations when you saw that something was missing?
  - ○ "That was hard because sometimes you thought it was new, and it wasn't when you turned it."
  - ○ "We just changed one cube at a time . . . Like if it was on top, we moved it to the other side or down one in the row."
- What were the easiest creations to make?
  - ○ "The ones that were all flat . . . Five cubes touching the table . . . No layers."
- What were the ones that you missed?
  - ○ "The ones that looked like they were in a mirror . . . Sometimes they were different, and sometimes they weren't."
- How did it help to review the creations of others when you couldn't touch them?
  - ○ "It helped sometimes, but other times we thought it [a shape] was new, and it wasn't. Ours was just turned different."
- How did it help when you could physically pick up the creations?
  - ○ "That was a lot better . . . We just kept turning them over to match ours."
  - ○ "Sometimes we moved ours to match theirs, and sometimes we moved theirs to match ours. Either way worked!"
- How did the drawings help you find all the ways?
  - ○ "Sometimes the drawings helped . . . Sometimes they didn't."
  - ○ "I wish we could have moved the drawings to see a cube that was hidden behind other ones."
  - ○ "It was good to see them. . . . We didn't have ones that matched all the pictures, so we made them."
- Do you think there are any more possibilities?
  - ○ "No . . . I don't think so."
  - ○ "Some of the drawings look the same . . . We think . . ."

Review the four-step procedure outlined above to facilitate sharing and comparing creations, the sample creations shown in figure 5.8, and the sample responses shown above to the questionnaire. Respond to the questions in Reflect 5.8.

Reflect 5.8

- How do you think each of the steps in the procedure would facilitate descriptions of the cube creations and their positions in space?

- What do you think students' comments about their final creations in response to the questionnaire indicate about their understanding of transformation and the way in which objects are positioned in space?

Although this task was difficult, students enjoyed it, and in fact they challenged the students in another second-grade class to try to find all the ways to make five-cube creations. Their ability to grasp ideas about transformation and notions about the unchanging, or invariant, character of a shape despite changes in its location or orientation in space certainly marked growth in their understanding. Structuring a three-dimensional object mentally, maneuvering it physically, and then matching it to a two-dimensional drawing were important experiences that fostered students' development of geometric understanding.

Summarizing Pedagogical Content Knowledge to Support Big Idea 3 through Essential Understandings 3*a* and 3*b*

Teaching the mathematical ideas in this chapter requires specialized knowledge related to the four components presented in the Introduction: learners, curriculum, instructional strategies, and assessment. The four sections that follow summarize some examples of these specialized knowledge bases in relation to Essential Understandings 3*a* and 3*b*. Although we separate them to highlight their importance, we also recognize that they are connected and support one another.

Knowledge of learners

This chapter has introduced tasks that illustrate young students' natural love of geometric learning and discovery. Research on young children has found that those who are learning motivated exhibit more persistence and have less chance of exhibiting "learned helplessness" than those who are performance oriented (Copley 1991). The tasks in this chapter provide many opportunities for students to discover new ideas without more formal, performance-based objectives. The students who worked through the look, make, and fix steps in task 17 were excited to see whether they could re-create the shapes they had seen and then adjust them if they needed to do so. In fact, this became one of their favorite daily activities! Tasks 18 and 19 engaged students in investigating shapes with mirror reflections and lines of symmetry, something with which they had little previous experience—and something that they discovered had endless possibilities. The mirrors and two-dimensional and three-dimensional shapes were added to centers, and students recorded drawings of their discoveries over a period of three months on a board titled "Discoveries We Have Made." Second graders tackled a very challenging problem in task 20 and showed persistence, along with some frustration and—when they had identified more than twenty-five unique solutions—great pride. The sharing of solutions was encouraged in many ways, and students solved the problem with the help of others. They found that help from one another could be very valuable in solving tough problems and that learning does not need to be an individual undertaking.

Knowledge of curriculum

As noted earlier, CCSSM does not include standards at the K–grade 2 levels that relate directly or formally to transformation, the focus of this chapter. Typically, exclusion from CCSSM means that textbooks and other curricular materials at these grade levels will follow suit, also omitting this topic. However, this does not mean that the information in this chapter should be ignored. What it does mean is that you will need to enhance tasks in your curricular materials to develop your students' understanding in this area. In addition, it means that your curricular tools will need to include such materials as manipulative shapes, mirrors, and three-dimensional connecting blocks for every student to handle and maneuver physically.

One particular curricular issue also needs to be addressed to avoid potential misunderstanding. Letters of the alphabet should not be used as objects to be reflected or oriented in different ways. Young students are learning that in some cases a change in the orientation of a letter shape signals an entirely different letter and associated sound, and they can then easily transfer that information to shapes and other objects, muddying their understanding. The reflection activities involving letters that Goldenberg and Clements (2014) include are excellent examples for adult learners but should not be used with young students in prekindergarten–grade 2.

Knowledge of instructional strategies

One of the most difficult decisions for a teacher to make is about when to intervene and when to stand by when students are exploring a mathematics concept or problem. When students exhibit frustration, should you give them a clue or word of encouragement, or should you ignore them and let them try to work through the frustration on their own? When students get sidetracked in an unproductive way, should you let them find their own dead end, or should you refocus them? When students are beginning to formulate an important idea, should you immediately provide praise for the idea, offer a positive but general comment, or just ignore them and give them time to make the connections for themselves? These intervention decisions are especially difficult with the types of tasks shared in this chapter. In the classroom where students worked on task 17, the teacher gave clues after she recognized a particular problem with the size of shapes. And when the students seemed to be overwhelmed by the number of shapes in the second picture, she counted them aloud so that everyone knew that they needed five shapes for their re-created picture. In working on tasks 18 and 19, students were at first voicing their discoveries quickly and not listening to others. The teacher decided not to intervene immediately and allowed them to concentrate on their own discoveries for a short time. While they were working, she recorded their comments as well as the ideas that she wanted to emphasize in the full-class discussion. After she brought the students together *without* their materials, she commented on the discoveries that they had made and, in some cases, asked students to demonstrate their specific discoveries. In planning for task 20, the teacher carefully thought out a series of verbal scaffolds that she would use when students reached points of frustration. While they were working on their creations, she went from group to group observing their work and commenting, "Oh . . . I haven't seen that one yet!" or "What an interesting one . . . I think it is unique," or "I think you already have that one in several places."

Knowledge of assessment

Observation is especially important as an assessment method in the tasks in this chapter. As indicated in the previous section, teachers may need to intervene after observing students' reactions to the task. Not every reaction can be predicted, and observation is key to assessing learners' dispositions as well as their understanding of concepts.

Videotape and scripts of student conversations and behaviors such as persevering are important tools for assessments that use observation. The scripting of the students' discoveries in tasks 18 and 19 helped the teacher identify those students who could use geometric vocabulary correctly and those who could not. It also allowed the teacher to review individual students' understanding because their comments could be labeled with the students' names (the names have been deleted from the work in figure 5.4 to protect students' privacy). Videotaping classroom activities like task 17 can allow the teacher not only to review instruction but also to see what individual students understand or do not understand. In addition, it allows opportunities to observe students who were quickly frustrated and those who were able to persevere.

Conclusion

The transformation activities in this chapter provide opportunities for students to discover the properties of an object that change or do not change when the object is transformed in some way. Students used concepts that they understood in making their discoveries in the tasks presented in this chapter. These discoveries, along with the understandings emphasized in chapters 1–4, are foundational to the essential understandings for geometry and measurement in grades 3–5 and on to grades 6–8.

into practice

Chapter 6
Looking Ahead with Geometry and Measurement

This chapter highlights ways in which the essential understandings discussed in Chapters 1–5 align with ideas that students develop after the prekindergarten–grade 2 years. The discussion demonstrates the importance of ensuring that young students develop a deep understanding of the essential concepts that serve as a foundation for subsequent learning.

Extending Knowledge of Geometry and Measurement in Grades 3–5

Learning in geometry and measurement in grades 3–5 is focused on more precise definitions and processes than students encountered in pre-K–grade 2. Students in grades 3–5 also expand their thinking about specific types of transformations and derive measurement formulas for both two- and three-dimensional shapes. The discussion that follows highlights four areas of focus in geometry and measurement in grades 3–5: (1) classification schemes based on defining properties; (2) transformations, with special attention to structure; (3) precision in specifying directions and distances; and (4) derivation of measurement formulas.

Classification schemes, defining properties, and specific relationships

Students in pre-K–grade 2 sort and categorize objects by attributes. At first, the attribute is usually stated, and then, when students have reached a later stage in their understanding, it is more precisely defined. In grades 3–5, students progress to classifying shapes with a focus on defining properties. Their developing understanding allows them, for example, to classify a square in a variety of ways and under a variety of names, all of which are dependent on specific defining properties. Figure 6.1 illustrates the classifying of examples and non-examples of squares that students become capable of doing in grades 3–5.

As the definitions in the figure illustrate, a square can be included and named in many classifications. The relationships between squares and non-squares, with some of the non-squares as quadrilaterals and some as other shapes, are more clearly understood in grades 3–5 than in the pre-K–2 years.

The equivalence relationship is also introduced in grades 3–5. For example, students investigate the relationship between two noncongruent triangles with the same base and height or two congruent rectangles in different orientations. Students in grades 3–5 define these equivalences in relation to area, a measurement concept that is only explored in in pre-K–grade 2 but is a critical area that is highlighted in grade 3.

As in pre-K–grade 2, investigations of shapes and classification schemes in grades 3–5 contribute to students' geometric understanding. Students who come to grade 3 after engaging in activities such as the tasks in this book are familiar with investigating shapes, transforming shapes in a variety of ways, and conjecturing about the possibilities. For example, a group of second graders who were accustomed to learning by investigating made a hypothesis about triangles after working with measuring worms of one-, two-, three-, and four-inch lengths. They used the worms to make as many different triangles as possible and recorded the arrangements that "worked" (that is, the endpoints met to form a triangle) and the ones that did *not* "work." Figure 6.2 shows the results of their exploration, on the basis of which the students made the following hypothesis: To make a triangle, the two sides that you put together need to be longer than the third side.

If students have a strong foundation of this sort, they can investigate polyhedra in grades 3–5, name shapes on the basis of defining attributes, and define terms like *straight, side, angle, face, vertex,* and *edge* more precisely. Students in grades 3–5 can also engage in the mathematical practice of defining. These investigations can initiate generalizations based on what they have experienced. Words like *all* and *some,* and phrases like "with the exception of," can support this work and the formation of hypotheses that can be tested.

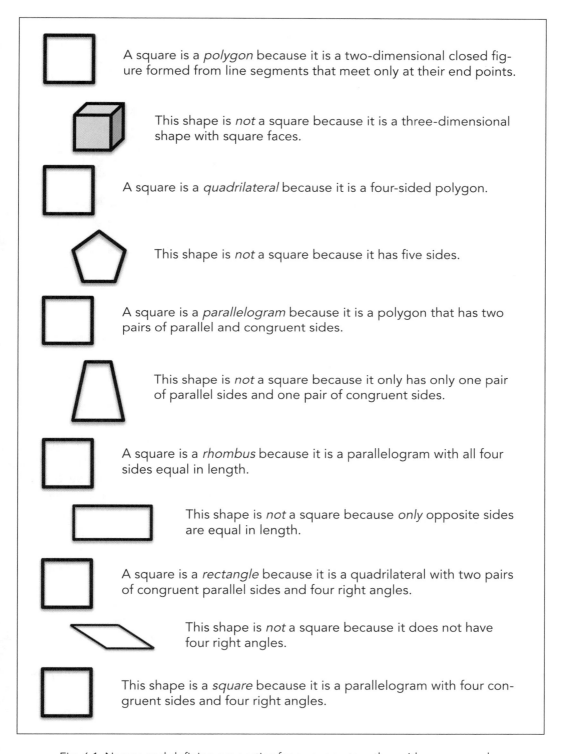

A square is a *polygon* because it is a two-dimensional closed figure formed from line segments that meet only at their end points.

This shape is *not* a square because it is a three-dimensional shape with square faces.

A square is a *quadrilateral* because it is a four-sided polygon.

This shape is *not* a square because it has five sides.

A square is a *parallelogram* because it is a polygon that has two pairs of parallel and congruent sides.

This shape is *not* a square because it only has only one pair of parallel sides and one pair of congruent sides.

A square is a *rhombus* because it is a parallelogram with all four sides equal in length.

This shape is *not* a square because *only* opposite sides are equal in length.

A square is a *rectangle* because it is a quadrilateral with two pairs of congruent parallel sides and four right angles.

This shape is *not* a square because it does not have four right angles.

This shape is a *square* because it is a parallelogram with four congruent sides and four right angles.

Fig. 6.1. Names and defining properties for a square, together with non-examples

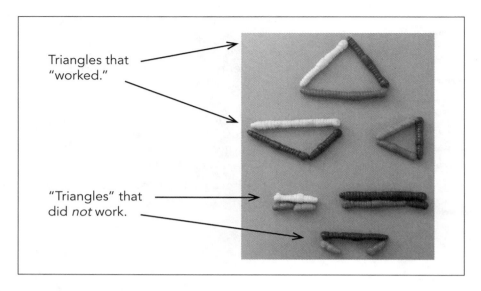

Triangles that "worked."

"Triangles" that did *not* work.

Fig. 6.2. Second graders' experimentation with one-, two-, three-, and four-inch measuring worms to make triangles

Transformation

Transformations are not a targeted topic in most mathematics programs for grades 3–5. In *Developing Essential Understanding of Geometry and Measurement for Teaching Mathematics in Grades 3–5*, however, Lehrer and Slovin (2014) emphasize that they are important for teachers of grades 3–5 to understand for their work with students in geometry and measurement. In fact, Lehrer and Slovin address this this topic in Big Idea 1: "Transforming objects and the space that they occupy in various ways while noting what does and does not change provides insight into and understanding of the objects and space." Third- through fifth-grade students' age-appropriate understanding of this first big idea and its associated essential understandings grows out of their involvement in investigations of change and invariance.

In pre-K–grade 2, students' work with transformations primarily consists of looking at shapes—both two- and three-dimensional shapes—from different viewpoints, using reflections and translations, and describing, with informal vocabulary, the attributes that change and those that do not change. In grades 3–5, students have had enough experience and developed sufficient understanding and skill to do activities that require them to "look for and make use of structure" and "look for and express regularity in repeated reasoning"—mathematical practices 7 and 8 in the Standards for Mathematical Practice in the Common Core State Standards for

Mathematics (National Governors Association Center for Best Practices and Council of Chief State School Officers [NGA Center and CCSSO] 2010). Investigations with transformations in grades 3–5 should support students' emerging awareness of the importance of noting attributes that change and those that do not under a transformation. Students' explorations with transformations should show them that examining structure and noting what changes or stays the same provide valuable information about the objects and the space that they occupy. Many investigations that support the big idea and associated understandings related to transformations also develop students' understanding of concepts related to measurement (for example, iteration and geometric relationships, including symmetry), as well as providing opportunities for students to use multiplicative reasoning.

Precision in specifying directions, routes, and locations

In pre-K–grade 2, students are introduced to the idea of structuring spaces to identify or locate objects. Foundationally, they are learning that they must know where they begin (the origin), where they should head (the direction), and how far they should go (the distance from the origin) to find an object on a coordinate graph. Because their understanding of the measurement process is limited, they often use imprecise or very general terms. In grades 3–5, students develop more precise language to specify directions and distances, as well as an understanding of fractions that enables them to measure parts of a whole unit with precision. For example, one group of second-grade students investigated the size of their playground to be sure that it would accommodate a new piece of equipment that they wanted to suggest that their local PTA purchase. They used metersticks to measure the length and width; however, their understanding of fractional parts of a meter was very limited, resulting in measurements like "a little more than 10 meters" or "about half of a meterstick." Fourth-grade students brought their more sophisticated understanding into play as they helped the second graders with the measurements, and, thanks to the fourth graders' greater experience and skill, a more precise diagram was presented to the PTA for consideration.

Deriving measurement formulas

The decomposition and composition of two- and three-dimensional shapes is a common activity in pre-K–grade 2, and the activities in Chapter 3 focus specifically on this topic. Students who have many experiences of interacting directly with materials and with one another as they decompose and compose shapes in the early years can build on these experiences in grades 3–5 to derive measurement formulas in a meaningful way. One familiar example of students' deriving a formula occurred during work on one of the tasks in this book. As second graders were making triangles for their pink and blue paper quilt by folding sticky notes in half (see fig. 3.12), their teacher continually reinforced the idea of one-half by asking how much of each small square on the quilt would be covered by one of the triangles. Students commented that a triangle is half of the square "when it is folded right." When asked what that meant, one student pointed to the vertices and said, "You hafta fold it at the points." The discussion continued the next day, with the students using rectangles of different sizes and folding them in half by "folding them right." The students' efforts to prove that these triangles matched perfectly also provided an example of the use of transformation. This decomposition experience provided an opportunity for older students, who were just beginning to understand the meaning of multiplication as an array, to derive the formula for the area of a triangle as $\frac{1}{2}(b \times h)$.

As students progress through the early years and into grades 3–5, their explorations offer many other examples of the development of their abilities to derive measurement formulas by decomposing and composing shapes. Decomposing the area of a regular hexagon (possibly represented by the yellow pattern block) into six equilateral triangles (green pattern blocks) can lead them to derive the formula of the area of a hexagon: $6 \times (\frac{1}{2} \times b \times h)$. Using the net of a cube and the measurement of just one side can help students derive the formula for the surface area of a cube: $SA = 6s^2$. Students can find the volume of a right rectangular prism by working with one-inch cubes and first filling one layer with cubes and then adding one layer of cubes after another until the prism is filled. After determining the volume of the prism by calculating the number of cubes needed to fill one layer and multiplying that number by the number of layers, students can generalize their work for any right rectangular prism, deriving the formula volume = length × width × height, or $V = lwh$.

Conclusion

The understanding of geometry and measurement that students develop in pre-K–grade 2 is foundational. If geometry and measurement are taught and learned with meaning, they can provide many opportunities for enhancing students' understanding in the intermediate grades. As the examples in this book have demonstrated, teachers need to devote considerable time and effort to ensure that their pre-K–grade 2 students develop understanding and skills that are sufficiently deep and robust to make these students successful in grades 3–5. As a teacher, you play a critical role in developing this important understanding through your insight into what your students currently know and don't know, your knowledge of your curriculum and careful selection of tasks, and your understanding and use of instructional strategies and assessments.

Appendix 1
The Big Ideas and Essential Understandings for Geometry and Measurement

This book focuses on the big ideas and essential understandings that are identified and discussed in *Developing Essential Understanding of Geometry and Measurement for Teaching Mathematics in Prekindergarten–Grade 2* (Goldenberg and Clements 2014). For the reader's convenience, the complete list of the big ideas and essential understandings in that book is reproduced below.

Big Idea 1. A classification scheme specifies for a space or the objects within it the properties that are relevant to particular goals and intentions.

Essential Understanding 1a. Mathematical classification extends and refines everyday categorization by making more precise what we mean by "sides," "angles," "straightness," or other features that we attend to as we categorize mathematical objects.

Essential Understanding 1b. We may classify the same collection of objects in different ways.

Big Idea 2. Geometry allows us to structure spaces and specify locations within them.

Essential Understanding 2a. To describe a location, we must provide a reference point (an origin) and independent pieces of information (often called *coordinates*) indicating distance and direction from that point.

Essential Understanding 2b. Geometry and measurement can specify directions, routes, and locations in the world—for example, navigation paths and spatial relations—with precision. Given a reference point and an orientation, we can label positions with numbers.

Essential Understanding 2c. Geometric objects are things that exist in our minds. Many of them are idealizations of things that also exist in the physical world.

Big Idea 3. We gain insight and understanding of spaces and the objects within them by noting what does and does not change as we transform these spaces and objects in various ways.

Essential Understanding 3*a*. Transformations can be used to describe differences between an idealized image of an object and the way that it is positioned in space or seen by the eye.

Essential Understanding 3*b*. Under each transformation, certain properties are invariant.

Big Idea 4. One way to analyze and describe geometric objects, relationships among them, or the spaces that they occupy is to quantify— measure or count—one or more of their attributes.

Essential Understanding 4*a*. Measurement can specify "how much" by assigning a number to such attributes as length, area, volume, and angle.

Essential Understanding 4*b*. Some quantities can be compared or measured directly, others can be measured indirectly, and the measurements of some objects are computed from other measurements.

Essential Understanding 4*c*. Measurement can be performed with a variety of units. The size of the unit and the number of units in the measure are inversely related to each other.

Essential Understanding 4*d*. Objects can be decomposed and composed to facilitate their measurement.

Appendix 2
Resources for Teachers

The following list highlights a few of the many books and articles that are helpful resources for teaching geometry and measurement in prekindergarten–grade 2.

Books

Brosterman, Norman. *Inventing Kindergarten*. New York: Kaleidograph Design, 2014.

Chapin, Suzanne H., and Art Johnson. *Math Matters: Understanding the Math You Teach, Grades K–8*. 2nd ed. Sausalito, Calif.: Math Solutions, 2006.

Copley, Juanita V. *Showcasing Mathematics for the Young Child: Activities for Three-, Four-, and Five-Year Olds*. Reston, Va.: National Council Teachers of Mathematics, 2004.

——. *The Young Child and Mathematics*. 2nd ed. Washington, D.C.: National Association for the Education of Young Children; Reston, Va.: National Council of Teachers of Mathematics, 2010.

Early Math Collaborative, Erikson Institute. *Big Ideas of Early Mathematics: What Teachers of Young Children Need to Know*. Boston: Pearson, 2014.

Fuson, Karen C., Douglas H. Clements, and Sybilla Beckmann. *Focus in Kindergarten: Teaching with Curriculum Focal Points*. Reston, Va.: National Council of Teachers of Mathematics; Washington, D.C.: National Association for the Education of Young Children, 2010.

Gavin, M. Katherine, Tutita M. Casa, Suzanne H. Chapin, and Linda Jensen Sheffield. *Designing a Shape Gallery: Geometry with the Meerkats*. M² Mentoring Young Mathematicians. Dubuque, Iowa: Kendall Hunt, 2010.

——. *Creating the School Measurement Fair: Measuring with Imi and Zani*. M² Mentoring Young Mathematicians. Dubuque, Iowa: Kendall Hunt, 2011.

——. *Exploring Shape Games: Geometry with Imi and Zani*. M² Mentoring Young Mathematicians. Dubuque, Iowa: Kendall Hunt, 2011.

——. *Using Everyday Measures: Measuring with the Meerkats*. M² Mentoring Young Mathematicians. Dubuque, Iowa: Kendall Hunt, 2011.

——. *Sizing Up the Lily Pad Space Station: Measuring with the Frogonauts.* M² Mentoring Young Mathematicians. Dubuque, Iowa: Kendall Hunt, 2012.

——. *Exploring Shapes in Space: Geometry with the Frogonauts.* M² Mentoring Young Mathematicians. Dubuque, Iowa: Kendall Hunt, 2013.

Keeley, Page, and Cheryl Rose Tobey. *Mathematics Formative Assessment.* Thousand Oaks, Calif.: Corwin; Reston, Va.: National Council of Teachers of Mathematics, 2011.

National Association for the Education of Young Children (NAEYC). *Exploring Math & Science in Preschool.* Washington, D.C.: NAEYC, 2015.

National Research Council. *Mathematics Learning in Early Childhood: Paths toward Excellence and Equity.* Committee on Early Childhood Mathematics, Christopher T. Cross, Taniesha A. Woods, and Heidi Schweingruber, eds. Center for Education, Division of Behavioral and Social Sciences and Education. Washington, D.C.: National Academies Press, 2009.

Pollman, Mary Jo. *Blocks and Beyond: Strengthening Early Math and Science Skills through Spatial Learning.* Baltimore: Paul H. Brookes, 2010.

Sarama, Julie, and Douglas H. Clements. *Early Childhood Mathematics Education Research: Learning Trajectories for Young Children.* New York: Routledge Taylor & Francis, 2009.

Chapter

Kersh, Joanne, Beth M. Casey, and Jessica Mercer Young. "Research on Spatial Skills and Block Building in Girls and Boys: The Relationship to Later Mathematics Learning." In *Contemporary Perspectives on Mathematics in Early Childhood Education*, edited by Olivia N. Saracho and Bernard Spodek, pp. 233–47. Charlotte, N.C.: Information Age, 2008.

Articles

Brown, Carmen S. "More than Just Number." *Teaching Children Mathematics* 15 (April 2009): 474–79.

Casa, Tutita M. "Capturing Thinking on the Talk Frame." *Teaching Children Mathematics* 19 (April 2013): 516–23.

Clements, Douglas H., and Julie Sarama. "Young Children's Ideas about Geometric Shapes." *Teaching Children Mathematics* 6 (April 2000): 482–88.

Copley, Juanita V., Kristin Glass, Linda Nix, Alison Faseler, Maria De Jesus, and Sheila Tanksley. "Measuring Experiences for Young Children." *Teaching Children Mathematics* 10 (February 2004): 314–19.

Dietiker, Leslie C., Funda Gonulates, and John P. Smith III. "Understanding Linear Measure." *Teaching Children Mathematics* 18 (November 2011): 252–59.

Minetola, Janice, Konnie Serr, and Laureen Nelson. "Authentic Geometry Adventure." *Teaching Children Mathematics* 18 (March 2012): 434–38.

Selmer, Sarah J., and Kimberly Floyd. "UDL (Universal Design for Learning) for Geometric Length Measurement." *Teaching Children Mathematics* 19 (October 2012): 146–51.

Tyminski, Andrew M., Monica Weilbacher, Nicole Lenburg, and Cindy Brown. "Ladybug Lengths: Beginning Measurement." *Teaching Children Mathematics* 15 (August 2008): 34–37.

Woleck, Kristine Reed. "Tricky Triangles: A Tale of One, Two, Three Researchers." *Teaching Children Mathematics* 10 (September 2003): 40–44.

Appendix 3

Tasks

This book examines rich tasks that have been used in the classroom to bring to the surface students' understandings and misunderstandings about geometry and measurement. A sampling of those tasks is offered here, in the order in which they appear in the book. At More4U, Appendix 3 includes all the tasks, some with black-line templates for classroom use.

Task 1

Sort and classify the shapes or solids identified below into groups. Use words to tell how you sorted the shapes.

Materials for this task:

- Attribute shapes (three colors—red, blue, yellow; four shapes—rectangle [that is not a square], square, circle, triangle [equilateral only]; two sizes—large and small [only one size is shown here])

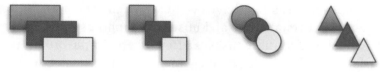

- Paper shapes (a variety, as pictured)

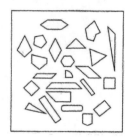

- Shapes and solids (a variety, as pictured)

- Shapes created with plastic straws with pipe cleaners threaded through them (a variety, as pictured; straw pieces are 2 inches, 4 inches, and 6 inches in length)

Task 4

Make, trace, draw, and describe three-dimensional shapes.

Task 6

Find or place the object or objects identified in each subtask, (a)–(e), below.

Locate _____ by using the spatial clues given:

a. An object by using 2-D or 3-D shapes and position words
    Sample:

Place the hippo

Clue: On top of the orange cube

b. An object hidden under ten cups in a number line

Sample clue: The bear is hidden under a cup *between* cup 3 and cup 8.

c. An object hidden on a multicolored 5 × 5 grid (shown here in gray scale)

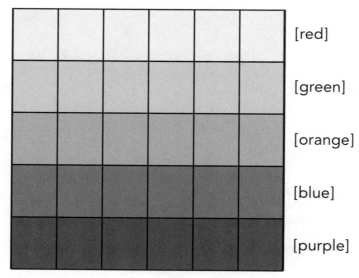

[red]

[green]

[orange]

[blue]

[purple]

Sample clue: The counter is in the orange row, in the third square.

Task 6, *continued*

d. Five objects in a horizontal, vertical, or diagonal line on a 5 × 5 grid

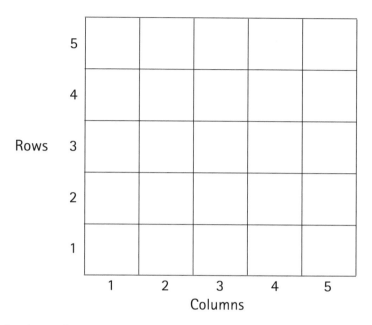

Sample clues: One penguin is in row 3 and column 4. Another penguin is in row 2 and column 4

e. Three 2-D or 3-D colored shapes on a grid of rows and columns. Trace the shapes, and color the squares within the outlines to match the color of the shape.

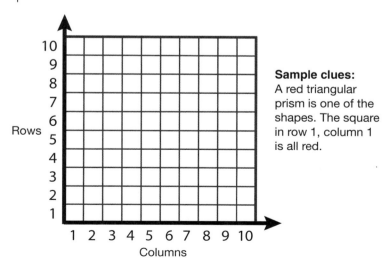

Sample clues:
A red triangular prism is one of the shapes. The square in row 1, column 1 is all red.

Task 9

Be an architect. Build a model building. Draw your building so that others can build it by using your plan [*or a photograph*].

Be a builder. Select an architect's plan [*or photograph*]. Build a building to match the plan. Show your building to the architect to see whether it matches his or her idea.

Task 13

Compare, using tools of your choice:

a. The sizes of five different pieces of fruit. Which one is the biggest? Which one is the smallest?

b. The heights of five block towers. Which tower is the tallest? Which tower is the shortest?

c. The capacities of four different-sized containers. Which container holds the most water? Which container holds the least water?

d. The volumes of two different boxes. Which box holds more cubes? Which box holds fewer cubes?

e. The areas of five 2-D shapes. Which shape covers the most space? Which shape covers the least space?

f. Angles that are right angles and angles that are not right angles. What angles can you find that have "special square corners"? What angles do not have "special square corners"?

Task 15

Big Bill and Little Larry measured the width and length of the classroom, using feet. Big Bill said the room was 26 feet wide by 38 feet long. Little Larry said the room was 52 feet wide by 76 feet long. Why did Big Bill and Little Larry get different answers?

Measure your room's length and width, and tell why your solution is correct. Use measuring tools of your choice.

Task 16

How far can the 3-D shapes shown below move (roll or slide) when released from the top of a ramp that is positioned at three different heights—6 inches, 12 inches, and 24 inches? Use any measuring tools of your choice. Record your results in the chart. Note that one shape—the cylinder—is oriented in two different ways for this task.

Height of ramp				
6 inches				
12 inches				
24 inches				

Task 19

Circle the 2-D pictures below that are symmetrical, and draw the lines of symmetry. Explain how you know that the shape is symmetrical.

References

Balfanz, Robert. "Why Do We Teach Young Children So Little Mathematics? Some Historical Considerations." In *Mathematics in the Early Years,* edited by Juanita V. Copley, pp. 3–10. Reston, Va.: National Council of Teachers of Mathematics, 1999.

Chapin, Suzanne H., and Art Johnson. *Math Matters: Understanding the Math You Teach, Grades K–8.* 2nd ed. Sausalito, Calif.: Math Solutions, 2006.

Clements, Douglas H., and Julie Sarama. *Learning and Teaching Early Math: The Learning Trajectories Approach.* New York: Routledge Taylor & Francis, 2009.

Copley, Juanita V. "The Effect of Success and Failure Experiences on the Task Achievement and Motivation of Learners with Performance and Learning Goal Orientations." PhD dissertation. Texas A&M University, 1991.

——. *Mathematics Institute for Pre-Kindergarten and Kindergarten: A TEXTEAMS Project.* Austin, Tex.: University of Texas, 1998.

——. *The Young Child and Mathematics.* 2nd ed. Washington, D.C.: National Association for the Education of Young Children; Reston, Va.: National Council of Teachers of Mathematics, 2010.

Dougherty, Barbara J. "Access to Algebra: A Process Approach." In *The Future of the Teaching and Learning of Algebra*, edited by Helen Chick, Kaye Stacey, Jill Vincent, and John Vincent, pp. 207–13. Victoria, Australia: University of Melbourne, 2001.

Dougherty, Barbara J., Alfinio Flores, Everett Louis, and Catherine Sophian. *Developing Essential Understanding of Number and Numeration for Teaching Mathematics in Prekindergarten–Grade 2.* Essential Understanding Series. Reston, Va.: National Council of Teachers of Mathematics, 2010.

Freudenthal, Hans. *Mathematics as an Educational Task.* Dordrecht, The Netherlands: Reidel, 1973.

Goldenberg, E. Paul, and Douglas H. Clements. *Developing Essential Understanding of Geometry and Measurement for Teaching Mathematics in Prekindergarten–Grade 2.* Essential Understanding Series. Reston, Va.: National Council of Teachers of Mathematics, 2014.

Grossman, Pamela. *The Making of a Teacher.* New York: Teachers College Press, 1990.

Hiebert, James. "Signposts for Teaching Mathematics through Problem Solving." In *Teaching Mathematics through Problem Solving Prekindergarten–Grade 6*, edited by Frank K. Lester Jr. and Randall I. Charles, pp. 53–62. Reston, Va.: National Council of Teachers of Mathematics, 2003.

Hill, Heather C., Brian Rowan, and Deborah Loewenberg Ball. "Effects of Teachers' Mathematical Knowledge for Teaching on Student Achievement." *American Educational Research Journal* 42 (Summer 2005): 371–406.

Lehrer, Richard and Hannah Slovin. *Developing Essential Understanding of Geometry and Measurement for Teaching Mathematics in Grades 3–5.* Essential Understanding Series. Reston, Va.: National Council of Teachers of Mathematics, 2014.

Magnusson, Shirley, Joseph Krajcik, and Hilda Borko. "Nature, Sources, and Development of Pedagogical Content Knowledge for Science Teaching." In *Examining Pedagogical Content Knowledge*, edited by Julie Gess-Newsome and Norman G. Lederman, pp. 95–132. Dordrecht, The Netherlands: Kluwer Academic, 1999.

National Council of Teachers of Mathematics (NCTM). *Curriculum Focal Points for Pre-kindergarten through Grade 8 Mathematics: A Quest for Coherence*. Reston, Va.: NCTM, 2006.

National Governors Association Center for Best Practices and Council of Chief State School Officers (NGA Center and CCSSO). *Common Core State Standards for Mathematics. Common Core State Standards (College- and Career-Readiness Standards and K–12 Standards in English Language Arts and Math)*. Washington, D.C.: NGA Center and CCSSO, 2010. http://www.corestandards.org

National Research Council. *Mathematics Learning in Early Childhood: Paths toward Excellence and Equity*. Committee on Early Childhood Mathematics. Christopher T. Cross, Taniesha A. Woods, and Heidi Schweingruber, eds. Center for Education, Division of Behavioral and Social Sciences and Education. Washington, D.C.: National Academies Press, 2009.

Pollman, Mary Jo. *Blocks and Beyond: Strengthening Early Math and Science Skills through Spatial Learning*. Baltimore: Paul H. Brookes, 2010.

Popham, W. James. "Defining and Enhancing Formative Assessment." Paper presented at the CCSSO State Collaborative on Assessment and Student Standards FAST meeting, Austin, Tex., October 10–13, 2006.

Sarama, Julie, and Douglas H. Clements. *Early Childhood Mathematics Education Research: Learning Trajectories for Young Children*. New York: Routledge Taylor & Francis, 2009.

Shulman, Lee S. "Those Who Understand: Knowledge Growth in Teaching." *Educational Researcher* 15, no. 2 (1986): 4–14.

———. "Knowledge and Teaching." *Harvard Educational Review* 57, no. 1 (1987): 1–22.

Van Hiele, P. M. *Structure and Insight: A Theory of Mathematics Education*. Orlando: Academic, 1986.

Wiliam, Dylan. "Keeping Learning on Track: Classroom Assessment and the Regulation of Learning." In *Second Handbook of Research on Mathematics Teaching and Learning*, edited by Frank K. Lester, Jr., pp. 1053–98. Charlotte, N.C.: Information Age; Reston, Va.: National Council of Teachers of Mathematics, 2007.

Yinger, Robert J. "The Conversation of Teaching: Patterns of Explanation in Mathematics Lessons." Paper presented at the meeting of the International Study Association on Teacher Thinking, Nottingham, England, May 1988.

Children's Books

Carle, Eric. *The Secret Birthday Message*. Reprint ed. New York: HarperCollins, 1986.

Jenkins, Steve. *Actual Size*. Boston: Houghton Mifflin Harcourt, 2004.

Titles in the Putting Essential Understanding into Practice Series

The Putting Essential Understanding into Practice Series takes NCTM's Essential Understanding Series to the next level through a focus on pedagogical content knowledge. Each volume builds on the companion volume in the earlier series to show teachers how to implement their understanding of mathematics in the classroom. The authors identify common misconceptions, along with strategies and activities to help students develop robust understanding through problem-based learning.

Putting Essential Understanding of—

Addition and Subtraction into Practice in Prekindergarten–Grade 2
ISBN 978-0-87353-730-8   Stock No. 14540

Geometry and Measurement into Practice in Prekindergartern–Grade 2
ISBN 978-0-87353-731-5   Stock No. 14541

Fractions into Practice in Grades 3–5
ISBN 978-0-87353-732-2   Stock No. 14542

Multiplication and Division into Practice in Grades 3–5
ISBN 978-0-87353-715-8   Stock No. 14347

Geometry and Measurement into Practice in Grades 3–5
ISBN 978-0-87353-733-9   Stock No. 14543

Ratios and Proportions into Practice in Grades 6–8
ISBN 978-0-87353-717-9   Stock No. 14349

Functions into Practice in Grades 9–12
ISBN 978-0-87353-714-8   Stock No. 14346

Statistics into Practice in Grades 9–12
ISBN 978-0-87353-737-7   Stock No. 14547

Geometry into Practice in Grades 9–12
ISBN 978-0-87353-736-0   Stock No. 14546

Forthcoming:

Putting Essential Understanding of—

Number and Numeration into Practice in Prekindergarten–Grade 2

Expressions and Equations into Practice in Grades 6–8

Geometry into Practice in Grades 6–8

Visit www.nctm.org/catalog for details and ordering information.

Titles in the Essential Understanding Series

The Essential Understanding Series gives teachers the deep understanding that they need to teach challenging topics in mathematics. Students encounter such topics across the pre-K–grade 12 curriculum, and teachers who understand the big ideas related to each topic can give maximum support as students develop their own understanding and make vital connections.

Developing Essential Understanding of—

Number and Numeration for Teaching Mathematics in Prekindergarten–Grade 2
ISBN 978-0-87353-629-5   Stock No. 13492

Addition and Subtraction for Teaching Mathematics in Prekindergarten–Grade 2
ISBN 978-0-87353-664-6   Stock No. 13792

Geometry and Measurement for Teaching Mathematics in Prekindergarten–Grade 2
ISBN 978-0-87353-665-3   Stock No. 13793

Rational Numbers for Teaching Mathematics in Grades 3–5
ISBN 978-0-87353-630-1   Stock No. 13493

Algebraic Thinking for Teaching Mathematics in Grades 3–5
ISBN 978-0-87353-668-4   Stock No. 13796

Multiplication and Division for Teaching Mathematics in Grades 3–5
ISBN 978-0-87353-667-7   Stock No. 13795

Geometry and Measurement for Teaching Mathematics in Grades 3–5
ISBN 978-0-87353-669-1   Stock No. 13797

Ratios, Proportions, and Proportional Reasoning for Teaching Mathematics in Grades 6–8
ISBN 978-0-87353-622-6   Stock No. 13482

Expressions, Equations, and Functions for Teaching Mathematics in Grades 6–8
ISBN 978-0-87353-670-7   Stock No. 13798

Geometry for Teaching Mathematics in Grades 6–8
ISBN 978-0-87353-691-2   Stock No. 14122

Statistics for Teaching Mathematics in Grades 6–8
ISBN 978-0-87353-672-1   Stock No. 13800

Functions for Teaching Mathematics in Grades 9–12
ISBN 978-0-87353-623-3   Stock No. 13483

Geometry for Teaching Mathematics in Grades 9–12
ISBN 978-0-87353-692-9   Stock No. 14123

Proof and Proving for Teaching Mathematics in Grades 9–12
ISBN 978-0-87353-675-2   Stock No. 13803

Statistics for Teaching Mathematics in Grades 9–12
ISBN 978-0-87353-676-9   Stock No. 13804

Mathematical Reasoning for Teaching Mathematics in Prekindergarten–Grade 8
ISBN 978-0-87353-666-0   Stock No. 13794

Visit www.nctm.org/catalog for details and ordering information.